The "Teaching of English" Series

General Editor—DR. RICHARD WILSON

LITTLE PLAYS FROM SHAKESPEARE

First Series

No. 104

Upper Stage

Rear Stage

Middle Stage

Front Stage

Yard

THE FORTUNE THEATRE

*(With acknowledgment to the publishers of
"Shakespeare's England.")*

LITTLE PLAYS

FROM

SHAKESPEARE

❧ FIRST SERIES ❧

Edited and
Arranged for Acting
by
EVELYN SMITH, B.A.

THOMAS NELSON & SONS, Ltd.
LONDON, EDINBURGH, AND NEW YORK

First published November 1926.
Reprinted April, November 1928 ; February 1930 ;
April 1931 ; October 1932 ; July 1933 ; July 1934 ;
October 1935 ; September 1936

PREFACE

MANY of Shakespeare's plays contain parallel plots, or main and sub-plot, or scenes which, with a little editing, have a clear dramatic interest even when isolated from their context. It is such plots and scenes which have gone to make these "little plays," which are intended primarily for acting, as finished productions in the school hall or informal ones in the school-room. But it is hoped that they may serve other purposes. Often, towards the end of term, when the Shakespeare "set book" has been carefully studied, something is wanted to occupy a few odd lessons. There is not time to embark upon a five-act play, and the reading of isolated unedited scenes has its obvious disadvantages. A little play may satisfactorily fill the gap, and add interest to the one studied in detail. *Henry V.*, for instance, is often set for examinations, and those who have read it may want to know more of Henry's youth than the comments made on it by the churchmen, and more of Falstaff than Mistress Quickly's account of his death. "The Adventure on Gadshill" will show the king's "wilder days," and the humour of the old rascal with whom he spent them, better than any lecture in class can do. The little plays may, again, serve as an introduction to the serious study of Shakespeare; they may be used on "Shakespeare nights" of the literary and dramatic society; and they should prove helpful in classes where the study of English literature presents serious difficulties.

The notes on costume roughly indicate the usual

stage dress of the characters of the plays. The question of elaborate and accurate costume depends entirely on circumstances, but even if the " dressing up " is to be of the simplest kind, it is well for the stage manager to have a clear idea of what he is aiming at. Period pictures can always be found in the school or town library, and these should be consulted, for, as every one who has played charades knows, a very slight disguise may give a most striking effect, if cleverly chosen.

However simply a play is to be produced, it should be shown against a good background—a clear wall space, or curtains of suitable colour and fabric. A wood or garden may be suggested by a frieze of boughs and two great jars of flowers set on supports, one on either side of the stage—big firm flowers that will last well. Rhododendrons are ideal for a formal garden scene. For a state scene two figures in bright tabards holding spears or banners, standing still as if carved from painted wood, should take the place of flowers. But each play will suggest its own decoration to the stage manager with an eye for a good effect.

Music is of great importance, and every one who teaches Shakespeare should send for Novello's catalogue of the settings of songs, overtures, dance music, and so on. In a boys' school a bugler will probably be found to give the " tuckets " and " sennets " which add so much to a stirring entrance ; girls must, as a rule, depend on the piano—but whatever instrument is available, music should be extensively employed. Often Shakespeare's songs are taught in singing lessons ; sometimes a boy or girl with a good voice and ear is capable of singing without accompaniment in the class-room, and the charm of the song sung need not be emphasized here. If it is at all possible, instrumental and vocal music should come in their right places in the most informal end-of-term readings of the play.

The directions given for tone of voice and gesture are, of course, not intended to be slavishly followed, but merely to serve as suggestions, which may be discarded for other interpretations more to the mind of stage manager or actor. The point is that there should be an interpretation—that, even for a one-lesson reading, parts should be assigned beforehand and " thought over " by those who are to take them, so that a good, lively rendering may be given to the audience.

CONTENTS

LITTLE PLAYS FROM SHAKESPEARE

THE TRICKING OF MALVOLIO

(From *Twelfth Night*)

PERSONS OF THE PLAY

OLIVIA, *a rich and beautiful Countess.*
SEBASTIAN, *betrothed to Olivia at the end of the play.*
SIR TOBY BELCH, *uncle to Olivia.*
SIR ANDREW AGUECHEEK, *a foolish knight.*
MALVOLIO, *steward to Olivia.*
FABIAN, *servant to Olivia.*
FESTE, *Olivia's fool.*
MARIA, *Olivia's attendant.*
Musicians of Olivia's household.

Situation : The other members of Olivia's household
heartily dislike her vain and affected steward Malvolio,
whom his mistress, while valuing him for the way in
which he discharges his duties, describes as " sick of self-
love." Matters come to a crisis in the first scene of the
following little play, and all those who have a grudge
against Malvolio plan a way of revenge.

Time of the events of the play : sixteenth century.
Time occupied in acting the play : one hour and a
quarter.

NOTE ON COSTUME

The men's dress consists of doublet and hose, shoes of
leather or other stuff shaped to the foot, ruff and cloak.
The doublet fits closely to the body, and the front may be

11

cut into a peak. The "upper hose" are wide breeches or "galligaskins," fastened to the doublet with tagged laces or "points." With these are worn the "lower hose" or long stockings, often of silk, of similar or contrasting colour. Hats are of stiff silk or velvet, with high crowns and narrow brims, or no brim at all. They are adorned with a jewel, or a wreath of tiny flowers in metal work. Ornaments are rings, watches, brooches, and long chains, with pendants, sometimes containing a portrait. Malvolio, until he decks himself out in his yellow stockings, is dressed all in black, with a plain gold chain and a white staff of office. The fashion of cross-gartering was that of tying the garters below and above the knee—not of the crossed thongs from knee to ankle, fashionable at an earlier time, with which Malvolio is sometimes incorrectly represented in drawings of the garden scene. Sir Toby's appearance is that of the bluff and jovial Elizabethan gentleman of middle age, who likes sport and a stoup of wine and a song, who praises the young woman he admires as "a beagle, true-bred," and abuses the man he dislikes as "a niggardly rascally sheep-biter." The "fashions of proud Italy," which may be supposed to be the general wear at Illyria, have little interest for him, and he may be attired in doublet and hose of frieze, of good cut, like that frieze jerkin of Sir John Harington's which won the approval of Queen Elizabeth, loose leather boots with straps, a small ruff, and a plain rather high-crowned hat with a feather. The clothes of Sir Andrew, the foolish gallant, are a little "wrong," as those of such a character invariably are, colour an uninteresting green or yellow, ruff not set stiffly enough, galligaskins not stuffed out to the proper proportion, cloak worn without the right jaunty gallantry. Although her grief is not spoken of in the scenes of this little play, Olivia is in mourning for the death of her brother, and it is usual for her household to wear black on the stage. Fabian's black doublet is cut very simply, his ruff is small, his upper hose not padded out to the round shape, and his lower hose gartered above the knee. Feste wears magpie motley of black and white, hung with bells, and a scarlet cockscomb on his jester's cap. He carries a bauble—a fool's head on a stick, or a coloured balloon. The musicians in the last scene, where Olivia is betrothed to Sebastian,

may be gaily attired in slashed or parti-coloured jerkins
with puffed sleeves, and hose of contrasted colours.
The grouping of these musicians, with their mock instru-
ments, may make a very pretty stage picture.

Olivia's dress is made with pointed bodice, puffed
sleeves, ruff, and skirt cut wide enough to hang in folds.
A richly wrought girdle is fastened in front of the dress,
reaching to the hem. Maria's gown, of some sort of
woollen stuff, is in the fashion of the time in its unexaggerated form—small ruff, tight bodice, wide skirt—and
she wears a narrow apron, and a handkerchief of silk or
fine linen bound over her head.

SCENE I

A room in OLIVIA'S *house. By an oaken table, on
which burn two candles in heavy chased candlesticks,
sits* SIR TOBY, *wine-cup in hand.*

[*Enter* SIR ANDREW, *rather unsteadily.*]

Sir To. [*with enormous geniality*]. Approach, Sir
Andrew ; not to be a-bed after midnight is to be up
betimes ; and " diluculo surgere," thou knowst—

Sir And. [*in a high squeaky voice, strongly contrasted
10 with* SIR TOBY'S *bluff tones*]. Nay, by my troth, I know
not : but I know, to be up late is to be up late.

[*With the satisfied air of one who has just voiced
an indisputable piece of wisdom, he seats himself at the table opposite* SIR TOBY.]

Sir To. [*shaking his head*]. A false conclusion : I
hate it as an unfilled can. [*Slowly and with husky
emphasis, determined to make his train of thought clear*]
To be up after midnight and to go to bed then, is
early : so that to go to bed after midnight is to go to

8. *Betimes*, Early.
8. *Diluculo surgere saluberrimum est*, To rise early is most healthful,
     a phrase from Lily's Latin grammar, once in common use in
     schools.

20 bed betimes.   Does not our life consist of the four
elements ?

Sir And. Faith, so they say ; but I think it rather
consists of eating and drinking.

Sir To. [*appreciatively*]. Thou'rt a scholar ; let us
therefore eat and drink.   [*Calling*] Maria, I say ! a
stoup of wine !

[*Enter, not* MARIA, *but* FESTE, *who sets two great flagons
on the floor.*]

Sir And. [*with a sort of crow*]. Here comes the fool,
30 i' faith.

Feste [*springing on the table, and thrusting his head,
with its fool's cap, between* SIR TOBY *and* SIR ANDREW].
How now, my hearts ! did you never see the picture
of " we three " ?

Sir To. [*in jovial delight*]. Welcome, ass.   Now,
let's have a catch.

Sir And. By my troth, the fool has an excellent
breast !   I had rather than forty shillings I had such a
leg, and so sweet a breath to sing, as the fool has.   In
40 sooth, thou wast in very gracious fooling last night,
when thou spokest of Pigrogomitus, of the Vapians
passing the equinoctial of Queubus : 'twas very good,
i' faith.   I sent thee sixpence for thy leman : hadst
it ?

Feste [*solemnly gabbling nonsense*]. I did impeticos
thy gratillity ; for Malvolio's nose is no whipstock :
my lady has a white hand, and the Myrmidons are no
bottle-ale houses.

---

20. *Four elements.* An old belief was that all existing things consist
     of these elements, earth, air, fire and water, which, in the
     human body, appear as bile, blood, choler, and phlegm.
26. *Stoup,* Cup.
34. *We three.* He is thinking of a painted signboard, inscribed " We
     be three," and showing two fools or asses—the reader being
     the third.
36. *Catch,* Part song, in which the singers sing the same melody, the
     second beginning the first line as the first begins the second,
     and so on.
38. *Breast,* Voice.   43. *Leman,* Sweetheart.

[*Takes up an empty wine-cup and peers into it*
50 *with a pathetic look.*

Sir And. [*filling the cup from one of the flagons*].
Excellent ! why, this is the best fooling, when all is
done. Now, a song.

[FESTE *closes his lips and shakes his head, as if it*
could not possibly be done.

Sir To. Come on ; there is sixpence for you : let's
have a song.

Sir And. There's a testril of me too : if one knight
give a—   [*Loses the thread of his own talk.*
60 *Feste* [*pocketing the sixpences*]. Would you have a
love-song, or a song of good life ?

Sir To. A love-song, a love-song.

Sir And. Ay, ay : I care not for good life.

Feste [*sings*]

O mistress mine, where are you roaming ?
O, stay and hear, your true love's coming,
That can sing both high and low :
Trip no further, pretty sweeting ;
Journeys end in lovers meeting,
70   Every wise man's son doth know.

Sir And. Excellent good, i' faith.

Sir To. Good, good.

Feste [*sings*]

What is love ? 'tis not hereafter ;
Present mirth hath present laughter ;
What's to come is still unsure :
In delay there lies no plenty ;
Then come kiss me, sweet and twenty,
Youth's a stuff will not endure.

80 *Sir And.* [*delighted*]. A mellifluous voice, as I am
true knight.

Sir To. [*sardonically*]. A contagious breath.

58. *Testril*, Sixpence.
65. *O mistress mine.* The various settings of the song are published
by Novello.

Sir And. Very sweet and contagious, i' faith.

Sir To. To hear by the nose, it is dulcet in contagion. [*With renewed hilarity.*] But shall we make the welkin dance indeed? shall we rouse the night-owl in a catch that will draw three souls out of one weaver? shall we do that?

90 *Sir And.* An you love me, let's do't: I am dog at a catch.

Feste. By'r lady, sir, and some dogs will catch well.

Sir And. [*with an expression of acquiescent wisdom, after giving the matter a moment's thought*]. Most certain. Let our catch be " Thou knave."

Feste. " Hold thy peace, thou knave," knight? I shall be constrained in't to call thee knave, knight.

Sir And. [*with an air*]. 'Tis not the first time I have constrained one to call me knave. Begin, fool: it begins, " Hold thy peace."

100 *Feste.* I shall never begin if I hold my peace.

[SIR ANDREW *looks slightly stunned, and then gives a shrill cackle of appreciation.*

Sir And. Good, i' faith. Come, begin.

[*Catch sung.*

Hold   thy peace! and I   pri-thee hold   thy peace,

Thou knave!   Hold thy peace, thou knave!   thou knave.

[*Enter* MARIA.]

Maria [*scolding, but not hostile*]. What a caterwaul-

86. *Welkin,* Sky.
87. *Weaver.* Many of the Elizabethan weavers were Calvinistic refugees who had fled from persecution in the Netherlands. A catch having the effect here described would be a wonderful catch indeed.

ing do you keep here ! If my lady have not called up
110 her steward Malvolio and bid him turn you out of
doors, never trust me.

Sir To. [*working it out*]. My lady's a Cataian, we are
politicians, Malvolio's a Peg-a-Ramsey, and [*with a
burst of delight*] " three merry men be we." [*Suddenly
extremely solemn.*] Am not I [*with difficulty*] con-
sanguineous ? am I not of her blood ? Tillyvally.
Lady ! [*Taking* MARIA *by the hand, and singing, with
much sentiment*] " There dwelt a man in Babylon,
lady, lady ! "

120 *Feste.* Beshrew me, the knight's in admirable
fooling.

Sir And. [*jealous, and yet striving to be impartial*].
Ay, he does it well enough if he be disposed, and so do
I too ; he does it with a better grace, but I do it more
natural.

Sir To. [*sings*]. " O, the twelfth day of December,"—

Maria [*snatching away her hand*]. For the love o'
God, peace !

[*Enter on the scene of revelry a gaunt and sombre figure,
130   that of the steward* MALVOLIO. *His feet are thrust
into heelless slippers, a dark gown envelops his
form, his sallow visage is surmounted by a nightcap
with a tassel. He holds a lighted candle. He eyes
the delinquents with stately disgust.*]

Mal. My masters, are you mad ? or what are you ?
Have you no wit, manners, nor honesty, but to gabble
like tinkers at this time of night ? Do ye make an
alehouse of my lady's house, that ye squeak out your
coziers' catches without any mitigation or remorse of
140 voice ? Is there no respect of place, persons, nor time
in you ?

Sir To. [*in righteous indignation*]. We did keep time,
sir, in our catches. Sneck up !

---

112. *Cataian*, Native of Cathay, or China—a term of contempt.
113. *Peg-a-Ramsey.* The name of an old ballad.
139. *Coziers*, Cobblers.   143. *Sneck up !* Go and be hanged !
(2,799)   2

Mal. Sir Toby, I must be round with you.   My lady bade me tell you that, though she harbours you as her kinsman, she's nothing allied to your disorders.   If you can separate yourself and your misdemeanours, you are welcome to the house ; if not, an it would please you to take leave of her, she is very willing to

150 bid you farewell.

Sir To. [*breaking into song, con molto sentimento*].

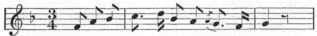

Fare-well, dear heart, since I must needs be gone,

Mar. [*reproving him in a half-hearted kind of way*]. Nay, good Sir Toby.

Feste [*taking* MALVOLIO *by the arm*].

His eyes do show his days are al - most done,

Mal. [*with tremendous dignity*].   Is't even so ?
Sir To. [*with happy resolution, waving an arm*].

But I will nev - er, nev - er, nev - er   die.

160   *Feste.*

O there, Sir To - by, there, O there, you lie.

[SIR TOBY *takes* MALVOLIO'S *other arm, and he and* FESTE *urge the resisting steward up the stage in a kind of barn dance.*
Mal. [*contriving to stand still, and speaking with bitter sarcasm*].   This is much credit to you.

144. *Round*, Plain-spoken.

Sir To. [*still singing*]. " Shall I bid him go ? "

Feste [*singing*]. " What an if you do ? "

Sir To. [*singing*]. " Shall I bid him go, and spare 170 not ? "

Feste [*singing*]. " O no, no, no, no, you dare not."

Sir To. [*suddenly wrathful, and on his dignity*]. Out o' tune, sir : ye lie. Art any more than a steward ? Dost thou think, because thou art virtuous, there shall be no more cakes and ale ?

Feste. Yes, by Saint Anne, and ginger shall be hot i' the mouth too.

Sir To. Thou'rt i' the right. [*With a lordly gesture*] Go, sir, rub your chain with crumbs. A stoup of wine, 180 Maria !

Mal. Mistress Mary, if you prized my lady's favour at any thing more than contempt, you would not give means for this uncivil rule : she shall know of it, by this hand.

[*With as much dignity of mien as he can summon he goes out.*

Maria [*snapping her fingers*]. Go shake your ears.

Sir And. 'Twere as good a deed as to drink when a man's hungry, to challenge him the field, and then 190 to break promise with him and make a fool of him.

Sir To. Do't, knight : I'll write thee a challenge ; or I'll deliver thy indignation to him by word of mouth.

Mar. Sweet Sir Toby, be patient for to-night. For Monsieur Malvolio, let me alone with him : if I do not gull him into a nayword, and make him a common recreation, do not think I have wit enough to lie straight in my bed : I know I can do it.

Sir To. Possess us, possess us ; tell us something of 200 him.

176. *Ginger,* Used for flavouring ale.
179. *Rub . . . crumbs.* The chain which was the steward's badge of office would be cleaned in this way.
196. *Nayword,* Byword.   197. *Recreation,* Laughing-stock.
199. *Possess us,* Tell us.

Mar. Marry, sir, sometimes he is a kind of puritan.

Sir And. [*with a shocked squeak*]. O, if I thought that, I'd beat him like a dog.

Sir To. What, for being a puritan! thy exquisite reason, dear knight?

Sir And. I have no exquisite reason for't, but I have reason good enough.

Mar. The devil a puritan that he is, or any thing constantly, but a time-pleaser, an affectioned ass, that 210 cons state without book and utters it by great swarths: the best persuaded of himself, so crammed, as he thinks, with excellencies, that it is his grounds of faith that all that look on him love him; and on that vice in him will my revenge find notable cause to work.

Sir To. [*who has listened to her description with nods of approval*]. What wilt thou do?

Mar. I will drop in his way some obscure epistles of love; wherein, by the colour of his beard, the shape 220 of his leg, the manner of his gait, the expressure of his eye, forehead, and complexion, he shall find himself most feelingly personated. I can write very like my lady your niece: on a forgotten matter we can hardly make distinction of our hands.

Sir To. Excellent! I smell a device.

Sir And. [*with a shrill crow of delight*]. I have 't in my nose too.

Sir To. He shall think, by the letters that thou wilt drop, that they come from my niece, and that 230 she's in love with him.

[*Slaps his leg, with a deep guffaw of enjoyment.*

Mar. My purpose is, indeed, a horse of that colour.

Sir And. And your horse now would make him an ass.   [*Chuckles, almost overcome by his own wit.*

Mar. Ass, I doubt not.

209. *Affectioned*, Affected.   210. *State*, Arguments of state.
210. *Without book*, By heart (an actor's phrase).
211. *Swarths*, Swathes of grass.

Sir And. O, 'twill be admirable !

Mar. Sport royal, I warrant you : I know my physic will work with him. I will plant you two, and let the fool make a third, where he shall find the 240 letter : observe his construction of it. Farewell.

[*Exit.*

Sir To. [*calling after her*]. Good-night, Penthesilea.

Sir And. Before me, she's a good wench.

Sir To. She's a beagle, true-bred, and one that adores me : what o' that ?

[*Tries to look completely indifferent, without noticeable success.*

Sir And. [*becoming sentimental and tearful*]. I was adored once, too.

250 *Sir To.* [*briskly*]. Let's to bed, knight. Thou hadst need send for some more money.

Sir And. [*vaguely*]. If I do not, never trust me, take it how you will.

Sir To. Come, come, I'll go burn some sack ; 'tis too late to go to bed now : come, knight ; come, knight.

[*He takes a cup of sack in one hand, and, with the
other arm, supports* SIR ANDREW, *and they go
out, in a slow, and, on the whole, stately manner,
260 singing a snatch of song.*

CURTAIN

242. *Penthesilea,* Queen of the Amazons, a race of virile women who devoted themselves to hunting and fighting. Sir Toby is teasing Maria, who is of diminutive stature.
254. *Sack,* Light dry Spanish wine. *Burnt* sack was mulled, *i.e.* warmed, sweetened, and spiced.

SCENE II

OLIVIA'S *garden. To the right centre is a box hedge.*
FABIAN *is peeping over this hedge, as if in expectation of
some one.*

[*Enter* SIR TOBY *and* SIR ANDREW *behind him.*]

Sir Toby [*slapping him on the shoulder*]. Come thy
ways, Signior Fabian.
Fab. [*ready for anything*]. Nay, I'll come : if I lose
a scruple of this sport, let me be boiled to death with
10 melancholy.
Sir To. Wouldst thou not be glad to have the
niggardly rascally sheep-biter come by some notable
shame ?
Fab. I would exult, man : you know, he brought
me out o' favour with my lady about a bear-baiting
here.
Sir To. To anger him we'll have the bear again ;
and we will fool him black and blue : shall we not, Sir
Andrew ?
20 *Sir And.* An we do not, it is pity of our lives.
Sir To. Here comes the little villain.

[*Enter* MARIA.]

How now, my metal of India ?
Maria [*with expression and gestures warning them to
be quick and quiet*]. Get ye all three into the box-tree :
Malvolio's coming down this walk : he has been
yonder i' the sun practising behaviour to his own
shadow this half-hour : observe him, for the love of
mockery ; for I know this letter will make a con-
30 templative idiot of him. [*They scuffle behind the box-
hedge, and she walks up and down to see if they are well
hidden.*] Close, in the name of jesting ! Lie thou there

---

12. *Sheep-biter*, A dog that worries sheep, hence a term of abuse.

[*throws down a letter*] ; for here comes the trout that must be caught with tickling.

[*Enter* MALVOLIO. *In his right hand he carries the steward's staff of office, a long white wand, and he walks with mincing dignity. All his gestures are those of the man who poses even when he is alone.*]

Mal. [*pausing to feast on his pleasant thoughts*]. 'Tis 40 but fortune ; all is fortune. Maria once told me she did affect me : and I have heard herself come thus near, that, should she fancy, it should be one of my complexion. Besides, she uses me with a more exalted respect than any one else that follows her. What should I think on't ?

Sir To. [*so indignant that he can scarcely contain himself*]. Here's an overweening rogue !

Fab. [*soothing him*]. O, peace ! Contemplation makes a rare turkey-cock of him : how he jets under 50 his advanced plumes !

Sir And. [*in imitative indignation*]. 'Slight, I could so beat the rogue !

Sir To. Peace, I say.

Mal. [*in the voice of one expressing the ultimate dream of ambition*]. To be Count Malvolio !

Sir To. [*furious*]. Ah, rogue !

Sir And. [*with a squeak of rage*]. Pistol him, pistol him.

Sir To. [*restraining him*]. Peace, peace !

60   *Mal.* There is example for't ; the lady of the Strachy married the yeoman of the wardrobe.

Sir And. [*not at all clear as to the allusion, but deeply shocked*]. Fie on him, Jezebel !

Fab. O, peace ! now he's deeply in : look how imagination blows him.

---

49. *Jets*, Struts.   50. *Advanced*, Puffed up.
60. *Lady of the Strachy.* Apparently this is one of the stories, fairly
    common in ballad and romance, in which the high-born lady
    weds the squire of low degree.
61. *Yeoman*, Servant.

Mal. Having been three months married to her, sitting in my state,—

Sir To. O, for a stone-bow, to hit him in the eye !

70 *Mal.* Calling my officers about me, in my branched velvet gown ; having come from a day-bed, where I have left Olivia sleeping,—

Sir To. [*to whom this is becoming past a joke*]. Fire and brimstone !

Fab. O, peace, peace !

Mal. [*lost in his dream*]. And then to have the humour of state ; and after a demure travel of regard, telling them I know my place as I would they should do theirs, to ask for kinsman Toby,—

Sir To. [*almost round the hedge*]. Bolts and shackles !

80 *Fab.* O, peace, peace, peace ! now, now.

[*Draws him back into hiding.*

Mal. Seven of my people, with an obedient start, make out for him : I frown the while ; and perchance wind up my watch, or play with my—some rich jewel. Toby approaches ; courtesies there to me,—

Sir To. [*with another start from hiding*]. Shall this fellow live ?

Fab. [*pulling him back*]. Though our silence be drawn from us with cars, yet peace.

90 *Mal.* I extend my hand to him thus, quenching my familiar smile with an austere regard of control,—

Sir To. [*fists clenched*]. And does not Toby take you a blow o' the lips then ?

Mal. Saying, " Cousin Toby, my fortunes having cast me on your niece, give me this prerogative of speech,"—

Sir To. What, what ?

Mal. " You must amend your drunkenness."

---

67. *State*, Chair of state.
68. *Stone-bow*, A crossbow for shooting stones.
89. *Cars.* A horrible punishment practised in ancient Rome was the tearing asunder of a man by binding him to two chariots which were driven in opposite directions.

Sir To. Out, scab !

100   *Fab.* [*pacifying him*]. Nay, patience, or we break the sinews of our plot.

Mal. " Besides, you waste the treasure of your time with a foolish knight,"——

Sir And. [*delighted*]. That's me, I warrant you.

Mal. " One Sir Andrew,"——

Sir And. I knew 'twas I ; for many do call me fool.

Mal. [*glancing down*]. What employment have we here ? [*Takes up the letter. Tense excitement behind the hedge.*]

110   *Fab.* Now is the woodcock near the gin.

Sir To. O peace ! and the spirit of humours intimate reading aloud to him !

Mal. [*almost losing his dignity in his excitement*]. By my life, this is my lady's hand : these be her very C's, her U's, and her T's ; and thus makes she her great P's. It is, in contempt of question, her hand.

Sir And. Her C's, her U's, and her T's ; why that ?

Mal. [*reads*]. " To the unknown beloved, this, and my good wishes : "——her very phrases ! [*Gazes at the* 120 *superscription.*] By your leave, wax. [*Is about to break the letter open, but pauses attracted by the seal.*] Soft ! and the impressure her Lucrece, with which she uses to seal : 'tis my lady. To whom should this be ? [*Carefully opens it.*]

Fab. This wins him, liver and all.

Mal. [*reads, in a rapt voice*].

> Jove knows I love :
> But who ?
> Lips, do not move ;
130 > No man must know.

---

110. *Gin*, Snare.   112. *Intimate*, Suggest.

122. *Impressure*, Impression of the seal. A common device for ladies' seals represented the Roman matron Lucretia, who ended her life by stabbing herself. This explains the " Lucrece knife " in the second of Maria's verses.

123. *Uses*, Is accustomed to.

" No man must know." What follows ? the numbers
altered ! " No man must know : " if this should be
thee, Malvolio.

Sir To. [*again aroused to fury by the complacency of
his countenance*]. Marry, hang thee, brock !

Mal. [*reads*].

> I may command where I adore ;
> But silence, like a Lucrece knife,
> With bloodless stroke my heart doth gore :
140 > M, O, A, I, doth sway my life.

Fab. A fustian riddle !

Sir To. Excellent wench, say I.

Mal. " M, O, A, I, doth sway my life." Nay, but
first, let me see, let me see, let me see.

Fab. What dish of poison has she dressed him ?

Sir To. And with what wing the staniel checks at it !

Mal. " I may command where I adore." Why, she
may command me : I serve her ; she is my lady.
Why, this is evident to any formal capacity ; there is
150 no obstruction in this : and the end—what should
that alphabetical position portend ? If I could make
that resemble something in me,—Softly ! M, O, A, I,
—[*Tries to puzzle it out.*]

Sir To. O, ay, make up that : he is now at a cold
scent.

Fab. [*confidently*]. Sowter will cry upon 't for all
this, though it be as rank as a fox.

Mal. M,—Malvolio ; M,—why, that begins my name.

Fab. Did not I say he would work it out ? the cur
160 is excellent at faults.

---

135. *Brock*, Badger.   146. *Staniel*, A kind of falcon.
146. *Checks.* The falcon is said to check when it forsakes the prey
    at which it is flown for another.
149. *Formal capacity*, Rational intelligence.
156. *Sowter ... cry upon ... faults*, Name of a hound ... give tongue,
    as a hound on the scent ... wrong trails. Sir Toby says
    that Malvolio is at a *cold* scent (one hard to find) ; Fabian
    that you can trust him to work out the *wrong* scent, though
    it be " rank as a fox " (Elizabethan hounds were trained to
    hunt stag or hare).

Mal. M,—but then there is no consonancy in the sequel; that suffers under probation: A should follow, but O does.

Fab. And O shall end, I hope.

Sir To. Ay, or I'll cudgel him, and make him cry O!

Mal. M, O, A, I; this simulation is not as the former: and yet, to crush this a little, it would bow to me, for every one of these letters are in my name. 170 [*Turning the letter over*] Soft! here follows prose. [*Reads*] " If this fall into thy hand, revolve. In my stars I am above thee; but be not afraid of greatness: some are born great, some achieve greatness, and some have greatness thrust upon 'em. Thy Fates open their hands; let thy blood and spirit embrace them; and, to inure thyself to what thou art like to be, cast thy humble slough and appear fresh. Be opposite with a kinsman, surly with servants; let thy tongue tang arguments of state; put thyself into the trick of 180 singularity: she thus advises thee that sighs for thee. Remember who commended thy yellow stockings, and wished to see thee ever cross-gartered: I say, remember. Go to, thou art made, if thou desirest to be so; if not, let me see thee a steward still, the fellow of servants, and not worthy to touch Fortune's fingers. Farewell. She that would alter services with thee,

"THE FORTUNATE UNHAPPY."

[*In a fever of excitement*] Daylight and champain discovers not more: this is open. I will be proud, I 190 will read politic authors, I will baffle Sir Toby, I will wash off gross acquaintance, I will be point-devise the very man. [*In triumph at his own sense and security*] I do not now fool myself, to let imagination jade me; for every reason excites to this, that my lady loves me.

---

161. *Consonancy,* Agreement.   167. *Simulation,* Disguise.
177. *Slough,* The snake's cast-off skin.
177. *Opposite,* Contradictory.   180. *Singularity,* Affectation.
188. *Champain,* Open country.   191. *Point-devise,* Exactly.

She did commend my yellow stockings of late, she did
praise my leg being cross-gartered ; and in this she
manifests herself to my love, and with a kind of in-
junction drives me to these habits of her liking.   I
thank my stars I am happy.   I will be strange, stout,
in yellow stockings, and cross-gartered, even with the
swiftness of putting on.   Jove and my stars be
praised ! Here is yet a postscript. [*Reads*] " Thou
canst not choose but know who I am.   If thou
entertainest my love, let it appear in thy smiling ;
thy smiles become thee well ; therefore in my presence
still smile, dear my sweet, I prithee." [*With a beatific
smile*] Jove, I thank thee : I will smile ; I will do
everything that thou wilt have me.

[*Is about to go out, in such eager haste that he forgets his staff of office, which he has laid down
while reading the letter, and trips over it.   That
calms his excitement a little, and, with a reproving gesture, he slowly picks up the staff, and goes
out with dignified gait, though still slightly
tremulous with the assurance of his great good
fortune.   The conspirators emerge from hiding,
in ecstasy at the success of the practical joke.*]

Fab. I would not give my part of this sport for a
pension of thousands to be paid from the Sophy.

Sir To. I could marry this wench for this device.

Sir And. [*not to be outdone*]. So could I too.

Sir To. And ask no other dowry with her but such
another jest.

Sir And. Nor I neither.

Fab. Here comes my noble gull-catcher !

[*Enter* MARIA.]

Sir To. [*seizing her by the hand, and kneeling before
her*]. Wilt thou set thy foot o' my neck ?

---

199. *Stout*, Haughty.   219. *Sophy*, The Shah of Persia.

Sir And. [*offering similar homage*]. Or o' mine
230 either ?

Sir To. Shall I play my freedom at tray-trip, and
become thy bond-slave ?

Sir And. I' faith, or I either ?

Sir To. [*rising, and taking her by the arm*]. Why,
thou hast put him in such a dream, that when the
image of it leaves him he must run mad.

Mar. [*delighted*]. If you will then see the fruits of
the sport, mark his first approach before my lady :
he will come to her in yellow stockings, and 'tis a
240 colour she abhors, and cross-gartered, a fashion she
detests ; and he will smile upon her, which will now
be so unsuitable to her disposition, being addicted to
a melancholy as she is, that it cannot but turn him
into a notable contempt. If you will see it, follow me.

Sir To. To the gates of Tartar, thou most excellent
devil of wit !

Sir And. I'll make one too.

[SIR TOBY *and* MARIA *go out left, arm in arm,* SIR
ANDREW *trailing after them.* FABIAN *goes out*
250 *right, alone.*

CURTAIN

SCENE III

*Another part of the garden. Left, on a stone seat, by
which grow tufts of flowers, sits* OLIVIA, *beautiful, but
languid and lovelorn.* MARIA *stands behind her, and
before her, cross-legged on the turf, sits* FESTE, *with a
stringed instrument. When the curtain has risen, he
stands and sings. In the play of "Twelfth Night" his
song is "Come away, death," which is sung to* OLIVIA'S

231. *Tray-trip*, A game at dice in which the lucky throw is a trey, or
three.

rejected wooer, the DUKE ORSINO. *In this little play, if*
10 *he is to sing to* OLIVIA, *a good song for him would be*
" Sigh no more, ladies, ladies, sigh no more," *from*
" Much Ado."   *Its setting is published by Novello.*

Olivia [*at the end of the song, gazing at a jewelled
miniature portrait she wears on a thin chain of pale gold*].
I have sent after him : he says he'll come ;
How shall I feast him ? what bestow of him ?
I speak too loud.   [*Glancing up.*
Where is Malvolio ? he is sad and civil,
And suits well for a servant with my fortunes :
20 Where is Malvolio ?
Maria [*as if she saw him approaching*]. He's coming,
madam ; but in very strange manner. He is, sure,
possessed, madam.
Olivia. Why, what's the matter ? does he rave ?
Mar. [*in amazement*]. No, madam, he does nothing
but smile : your ladyship were best to have some
guard about you, if he come ; for, sure, the man is
tainted in his wits.
Olivia [*impatiently*]. Go call him hither. [*Exit*
30 MARIA.] I am as mad as he,
If sad and merry madness equal be.

[MARIA *comes in, with the expression of one resolved
    not to smile at all costs. She is followed by* MAL-
    VOLIO, *walking with little mincing steps, hand
    on heart, face wreathed in smiles. He wears
    yellow stockings and cross garters.*]

How now, Malvolio !
Mal. [*after an elaborate bow*]. Sweet lady, ho, ho.
Oli. [*puzzled*]. Smilest thou ?
40 I sent for thee upon a sad occasion.
Mal. Sad, lady ! I could be sad ; this does make
some obstruction in the blood, this cross-gartering ;
but what of that ? [*meaningly*] if it please the eye of

18. *Sad*, Grave.

one, it is with me as the very true sonnet is, " Please one, and please all." [*Kisses his hand.*

Oli. Why, how dost thou, man ? what is the matter with thee ?

Mal. [*with an attempt at airiness*]. Not black in my mind, though yellow in my legs. [*Smiling, and in a* 50 *bantering tone, as he presses his hand to his heart, where the letter lies hidden.*] It did come to his hands, and commands shall be executed : [*most insinuatingly*] I think we do know the sweet Roman hand.

Oli. God comfort thee ! Why dost thou smile so and kiss thy hand so oft ?

Mar. [*in a tone of deepest concern*]. How do you, Malvolio ?

Mal. [*with a complete change of manner, drawing himself up and eyeing* MARIA *as if determined to put her* 60 *in her place*]. At your request ! yes ; nightingales answer daws.

Mar. Why appear you with this ridiculous boldness before my lady ?

Mal. [*to* OLIVIA]. " Be not afraid of greatness " : 'twas well writ.

Oli. [*trying to humour him*]. What meanest thou by that, Malvolio ?

Mal. " Some are born great,"—

Oli. Ha !

70   *Mal.* " Some achieve greatness,"—

Oli. What sayest thou ?

Mal. " And some have greatness thrust upon them." [*Smiles, as he fancies, irresistibly.*

Oli. [*really troubled*]. Heaven restore thee !

Mal. " Remember who commended thy yellow stockings,"—

Oli. [*more than ever at sea*]. Thy yellow stockings !

Mal. " And wished to see thee cross-gartered."

---

53. *Roman hand.* In the sixteenth century the Italian and Roman handwriting became fashionable in England.

Oli. Cross-gartered!

80   *Mal.* " Go to, thou art made, if thou desirest to be so,"—

Oli. Am I made ?

Mal. " If not, let me see thee a servant still."

Oli. Why, this is very midsummer madness.

[*Enter* FABIAN.]

Fab. Madam, the young gentleman of the Count Orsino's is returned : he attends your ladyship's pleasure.

Oli. I'll come to him. [*Exit* FABIAN.] Good Maria, 90 let this fellow be looked to. Where's my cousin Toby? Let some of my people have a special care of him : I would not have him miscarry for the half of my dowry.

[*Gives a concerned glance towards* MALVOLIO, *and at once turns her head as he simpers and kisses his hand, and goes out with* MARIA.

Mal. [*in high feather*]. O, ho ! do you come near me now ? no worse man than Sir Toby to look to me ! This concurs directly with the letter : she sends him on purpose, that I may appear stubborn to him ; for 100 she incites me to that in the letter. "Cast thy humble slough," says she ; " be opposite with a kinsman, surly with servants ; let thy tongue tang with arguments of state ; put thyself into the trick of singularity ; " and consequently sets forth the manner how ; as, a sad face, a reverend carriage, a slow tongue, in the habit of some sir of note, and so forth.   I have limed her ; but [*with a burst of proper humility*] it is Jove's doing, and Jove make me thankful ! [*Returning to the consideration of how convincing it all is*] And 110 when she went away now, " Let this *fellow* be looked to " : *fellow !* not Malvolio, nor after my degree, but *fellow.* Why, everything adheres together, that no

92. *Miscarry*, Come to harm.
106. *Limed her*, Caught her, as a bird is trapped with bird-lime.

dram of a scruple, no scruple of a scruple, no obstacle,
no incredulous or unsafe circumstance—What can be
said ? Nothing that can be can come between me
and the full prospect of my hopes. Well, Jove, not
I, is the doer of this, and he is to be thanked.

[*Enter* MARIA, *with the warning look and gesture of one
  admitting visitors to a dangerous case, followed by*
120 SIR TOBY, *bracing himself up as if to risk his life
  in a good cause, and* FABIAN *walking on tiptoe.*]

Sir To. Which way is he, in the name of sanctity ?
If all the devils of hell be drawn in little, and Legion
himself possessed him, yet I'll speak to him.

Fab. Here he is, here he is. [*Very gently and tact-
fully*] How is't with you, sir ? how is't with you,
man ?

Mal. [*with a stately gesture*]. Go off ; I discard you :
let me enjoy my private : go off.

130 *Mar.* [*much concerned*]. Lo, how hollow the fiend
speaks within him ! Did not I tell you ? Sir Toby,
my lady prays you to have a care of him.

Mal. [*with satisfaction*]. Ah, ha, does she so ?

Sir To. [*waving them off*]. Go to, go to ; peace,
peace ; we must deal gently with him : let me alone.
[*Approaches* MALVOLIO] How do you, Malvolio ? how
is't with you ? [*In tones of pious exhortation*] What,
man ! defy the devil : consider, he's an enemy to man-
kind.

140 *Mal.* [*in a terrible voice*]. Do you know what you
say ?

[*The three scuffle to one side of the stage as if in
  mortal terror of the madman.*

Mar. La you, an you speak ill of the devil, how he
takes it at heart ! Pray God, he be not bewitched !
My lady would not lose him for more than I can say.

---

130. *The fiend.* The old belief was that the madman was possessed
      by a devil.
    (2,799)   3

Mal. [*approaching her*]. How now, mistress !

Mar. [*taking refuge behind* SIR TOBY]. O Lord !

Sir To. [*rebuking them*]. Prithee, hold thy peace ;
150 this is not the way : do you not see you move him ?
let me alone with him.

Fab. No way but gentleness ; gently, gently : the
fiend is rough, and will not be roughly used.

Sir To. [*in a wheedling voice, as if he were speaking
to a small child*]. Why, how now, my bawcock ! how
dost thou, chuck ?

Mal. [*all his outraged dignity in the one word*]. Sir !

Sir To. [*still coaxing him*]. Ay, Biddy, come with
me.   [*Changing his tone*] What, man ! 'tis not for
160 gravity to play at cherry-pit with Satan : hang him,
foul collier !

Mar. Get him to say his prayers, good Sir Toby,
get him to pray.

Mal. My prayers, minx !

Mar. [*sadly, shaking her head*]. No, I warrant you,
he will not hear of godliness.

Mal. [*unable to endure any more*]. Go, hang yourselves all ! you are idle shallow things : I am not of
your element : you shall know more hereafter.

170   [*He stalks out, the three collapse in the various atti-
tudes of those overcome with mirth.*

Sir To. [*wiping his eyes*]. Is't possible ?

Fab. If this were played upon a stage now, I could
condemn it as an improbable fiction.

Sir To. His very genius hath taken the infection of
the device, man.

Mar. Nay, pursue him now, lest the device take
air and taint.

---

155. *Bawcock*, Fine fellow ; *Chuck*, Chick— colloquial terms of endearment, most unsuitable for the dignified Malvolio.

160. *Cherry-pit*, A game in which cherry-stones are pitched into a
hole.

175. *Genius*, The guardian spirit formerly supposed to dwell with
man and control his actions.

177. *Take air and taint*, Become exposed and ruined.

Fab. Why, we shall make him mad indeed.

180   *Mar.* The house will be the quieter.

Sir To. Come, we'll have him in a dark room and bound, and the fool shall visit him in the guise of a priest. My niece is already in the belief that he's mad : we may carry it thus, for our pleasure and his penance, till our very pastime, tired out of breath, prompt us to have mercy on him : at which time we will bring the device to the bar and crown thee for a finder of madmen.   [*They go out together, in high glee.*

CURTAIN

SCENE IV

OLIVIA'S *garden.* OLIVIA *sits on the stone bench,* SEBASTIAN, *to whom she is just betrothed, at her feet. Soft music, as if played by the attendants of the countess, grouped at the other side of the stage.*

Oli. [*to* SEBASTIAN, *as the music dies away*]. How dost thou like this tune ?

Seb. It gives a very echo to the seat
Where love is throned.

10   *Oli.*   Thou dost speak masterly.
To-night we'll feast with music. [*To* Attendant] Fetch
      Malvolio hither :
And yet, alas, now I remember me,
They say, poor gentleman, he's much distract.

    [*Enter* FESTE *with a letter, and* FABIAN.]

[*Looking fondly at* SEBASTIAN] A most extracting
      frenzy of mine own
From my remembrance clearly banish'd his.
[*To* FESTE] How does he, sirrah ?

20   *Feste.* Truly, madam, he holds Beelzebub at the

---

6. *How dost . . . masterly.* These lines really belong to Orsino and
    Viola, who do not appear in this shortened version of the play.
16. *Extracting,* Absorbing.

stave's end as well as man in his case may do : has
here writ a letter to you ; I should have given 't you
to-day morning, but as a madman's epistles are no
gospels, so it skills not much when they are delivered.

Oli. Open 't, and read it.

Feste. Look then to be well edified when the fool
delivers the madman. [*Reads, with what he fancies a
madman's gesture and in a frenzied voice*] " By the
Lord, madam,"—

30 *Oli.* How now ! art thou mad ?

Feste. No, madam, I do but read madness : an your
ladyship will have it as it ought to be, you must allow
Vox.

Oli. Prithee, read i' thy right wits.

Feste. So do I, madonna ; but to read his right wits
is to read thus : therefore perpend, my princess, and
give ear.

Oli. [*impatiently, to* FABIAN]. Read it you, sirrah.

Fab. [*reads*]. " By the Lord, madam, you wrong me,
40 and the world shall know it : though you have put me
into darkness and given your drunken cousin rule over
me, yet have I the benefit of my senses as well as your
ladyship.   I have your own letter that induced me to
the semblance I put on : with the which I doubt not
but to do myself much right, or you much shame.
Think of me as you please.   I leave my duty a little
unthought of and speak out of my injury.

" THE MADLY-USED MALVOLIO."

Oli. [*to* FESTE]. Did he write this ?

50 *Feste.* Ay, madam.

Seb. This savours not much of distraction.

Oli. See him deliver'd, Fabian ; being him hither.

[*Exit* FABIAN, *and re-enters with* MALVOLIO,
*slightly draggled and dishevelled in appearance,
but obviously sane.*

---

24. *Skills not,* Does not matter.   27. *Delivers,* Utters the words of.
33. *Vox,* The (appropriate) voice.   36. *Perpend,* Consider.

Seb. Is this the madman?

Oli.   Ay, my lord, this same.

[*In a gentle voice*] How now, Malvolio?

Mal. Madam, you have done me wrong,
60 Notorious wrong.

Oli.   Have I, Malvolio? no.

Mal. Lady, you have. Pray you, peruse that
    letter.

        [*Gives her that which he found in the garden.*

You must not now deny it is your hand :
Write from it, if you can, in hand or phrase ;
Or say 'tis not your seal, not your invention.
You can say none of this : well, grant it then
And tell me, in the modesty of honour,
70 Why you have given me such clear lights of favour,
Bade me come smiling and cross-garter'd to you,
To put on yellow stockings and to frown
Upon Sir Toby and the lighter people ;
And, acting this in an obedient hope,
Why have you suffer'd me to be imprison'd,
Kept in a dark house, visited by the priest,
And made the most notorious geck and gull
That e'er invention play'd on ? tell me why.

Oli. Alas, Malvolio, this is not my writing,
80 Though, I confess, much like the character :
But, out of question, 'tis Maria's hand.
And now I do bethink me, it was she
First told me thou wast mad ; thou camest in smiling,
And in such forms which here were presupposed
Upon thee in the letter. Prithee, be content :
This practice hath most shrewdly pass'd upon thee ;
But when we know the grounds and authors of it,
Thou shalt be both the plaintiff and the judge
Of thine own cause.

90 *Fab.* [*coming forward*]. Good madam, hear me
    speak,

69. *Modesty*, Plain unexaggerated statement.   77. *Geck*, Dupe
86. *Practice*, Plot.   86. *Shrewdly*, Cruelly.

And let no quarrel nor no brawl to come
Taint the condition of this present hour,
Which we all joy at.   In hope it shall not so,
Most freely I confess, myself and Toby
Set this device against Malvolio here,
Upon some stubborn and uncourteous parts
We had conceived against him : Maria writ
The letter at Sir Toby's great importance ;
100 In recompense whereof he hath married her.
How with a sportful malice it was follow'd,
May rather pluck on laughter than revenge ;
If that the injuries be justly weigh'd
That have on both sides pass'd.

Oli. [*pityingly, almost tenderly*]. Alas, poor fool, how
have they baffled thee !

Feste [*imitating* MALVOLIO]. Why, " some are born
great, some achieve greatness, and some have greatness thrown upon them."   I was one, sir, in this inter-
110 lude ; one Sir Topas the priest, who visited you in
your affliction, sir ; but that's all one.   But do you
remember ?   [*Imitating* MALVOLIO's *tone of distaste for
him and his fooling*] " Madam, why laugh you at such
a barren rascal ? an you smile not, he's gagged " ;
[*tapping* MALVOLIO's *shoulder with his bauble*] and
thus the whirligig of time brings in his revenges.

Mal. [*in miserable fury*]. I'll be revenged on the
whole pack of you.   [*Exit.*

Oli. He hath been most notoriously abused.

120   *Seb.* Let's follow and entreat him to a peace.
When that is made, and golden time convents,
A solemn combination shall be made
Of our dear souls.   Come, sweet Olivia.

[*They go out, followed by* FABIAN *and the* Musicians.
FESTE *prances to the centre of the stage and
sings his farewell song.*

99. *Importance,* Importunity, eager request.
106. *Baffled,* Treated shamefully.   109. *Interlude,* Little play.
116. *Whirligig,* Spinning-top.

When that I was and a little tiny boy,
    With hey, ho, the wind and the rain,
A foolish thing was but a toy,
130   For the rain it raineth every day.

But when I came to man's estate,
    With hey, ho, the wind and the rain,
'Gainst knaves and thieves men shut their gate,
    For the rain it raineth every day.

But when I came, alas! to wive,
    With hey, ho, the wind and the rain,
By swaggering could I never thrive,
    For the rain it raineth every day.

A great while ago the world begun,
140   With hey, ho, the wind and the rain,
But that's all one, our play is done,
    And we'll strive to please you every day.
        [*Makes a deep bow to the audience.*

CURTAIN

THE SHREW TAMED

(The Petruchio and Katharina story from *The Taming of the Shrew*.)

PERSONS OF THE PLAY

BAPTISTA, *a rich gentleman of Padua.*
KATHARINA, }
BIANCA, } *his daughters.*
LUCENTIO, *in love with Bianca.*
PETRUCHIO, *suitor to Katharina.*
HORTENSIO, *friend to Lucentio and Petruchio*
A Tutor.
A Tailor.
A Haberdasher.
* ROSINA, *wife of Hortensio.*
† SERVANTS : BIONDELLO, *servant to Lucentio* ; GRUMIO, CURTIS, NATHANIEL, PETER, PHILIP, JOSEPH, *and* NICHOLAS, *servants to Petruchio* ; attendants on Baptista.
Wedding guests.

Situation.—Bianca is wooed by many suitors, but Baptista refuses to give his consent to her marriage until her elder sister Katharina is wedded. Katharina's shrewish disposition makes her as much feared as her sister is loved, and she has no suitors, until one Petruchio, a gentleman of Verona, woos her and undertakes to

---

* This character is designated " widow " in Shakespeare's play, but as Hortensio's story is omitted from these scenes, she is introduced under a definite name.
† The number of servants may, of course, be reduced according to the size of the stage or the number of actors available.

" tame " her. How he achieves this task is the story of this little play.

Time of the story of the play : sixteenth century.
Time occupied in acting the play : one hour and a quarter.

NOTE ON COSTUME

Baptista wears a gown reaching to the ankles, slightly shaped in at the waist, and trimmed with fur. The long hanging sleeves are cut away to show tight under-sleeves. His hat is like that of a beefeater at the Tower. The young men wear doublets and hose, flat shoes with slightly pointed toes, small ruffs, and rather high-crowned, narrow-brimmed hats, adorned with a feather. Petruchio's get-up for his wedding is described in the course of the play. The Tutor wears an academic gown. The dress of the Tailor and Haberdasher consists of a tight-fitting doublet of sober hue, made longer than that worn by Petruchio and his friends, a leather belt, grey stockings and shoes, and a flat cap. The servants are clad in blue liveries, with hanging shoulder-sleeves on which the arms of their master are embroidered. The trunk hose worn by young men of the upper and middle classes are padded, those of the servants are limp, and their stockings are kept up with woollen garters tied above the knee.

Women's dress consists of a hooped skirt with a long, stiff, pointed bodice, and puffed, slashed sleeves. Sometimes the skirt was made with a wide centre panel of another colour, repeated in the lining shown where the sleeves were slashed. Small ruffs are more becoming and more comfortable than the very large ones. The cap about which there is so much to-do in Scene IV. is a tiny hood of stiff silk, or what is called the " Juliet cap "—Petruchio's contemptuous and vivid description of it best fits the latter fashion.

Katharina's wedding dress is of white or russet, adorned with favours of ribbon twisted into the form of true lover's knots. The colours of a bride's favours were blue, red, peach, orange, tawny, flame, or white. After the ceremony was ended, these favours were distributed among the guests.

SCENE I

A room in BAPTISTA'S *house.*

[*Enter* KATHARINA, *tall, dark, and not unbeautiful, but disfigured by her angry and sullen expression. She drags with her her younger sister,* BIANCA, *whose hands she has bound together with cords.*]

   Bian. [*half crying*]. Good sister, wrong me not, nor
      wrong yourself.
To make a bondmaid and a slave of me ;
10 That I disdain : but for these other gawds,
     [*Lifting her hands so that the jewels she wears are
     clearly seen.*
Unbind my hands, I'll pull them off myself,
Yea, all my raiment, to my petticoat ;
Or what you will command me will I do,
So well I know my duty to my elders.
   Kath. [*taking her by the shoulders*]. Of all thy
     suitors, here I charge thee, tell
Whom thou lovest best : see thou dissemble not.
20 *Bian.* Believe me, sister, of all the men alive
I never yet beheld that special face
Which I could fancy more than any other.
   Kath. [*shaking her*]. Minion, thou liest. Is't not
     Francisco ?
   Bian. If you affect him, sister, here I swear
I'll plead for you myself, but you shall have him.
   Kath. O then, belike you fancy riches more :
You will have Gremio to keep you fair.
   Bian. Is it for him you do envy me so ?
30 Nay then you jest, and now I well perceive

    10. *Gawds,* Ornaments.
    23. *Minion,* Darling, little favourite (used contemptuously).
    25. *Affect,* Have an inclination for.

You have but jested with me all this while :
I prithee, sister Kate, untie my hands.

    Kath. [*furiously*]. If that be jest, then all the rest
    was so.   [*Strikes her.*

            [*Enter* BAPTISTA.]

    Bap. Why, how now, dame ! whence grows this
      insolence ?
Bianca, stand aside. Poor girl, she weeps.
                    [*He unties the cords.*
40 [*To* BIANCA] Go ply thy needle ; meddle not with her.
[*To* KATE] For shame, thou hilding of a devilish spirit,
Why dost thou wrong her that did ne'er wrong thee ?
When did she cross thee with a bitter word ?

    Kath. Her silence flouts me, and I'll be revenged.
                [*Flies after* BIANCA.

    Bap. What, in my sight ?—Bianca, get thee in.
                [*Exit* BIANCA.

    Kath. [*standing heaving with rage, glaring at her
    father*] :
50 What, will you not suffer me ? Nay, now I see
She is your treasure, she must have a husband ;
I must dance barefoot on her wedding day,
And for your love to her lead apes in hell.
Talk not to me : I will go sit and weep
Till I can find occasion of revenge.   [*Exit.*

    Bap. [*beside himself*]. Was ever gentleman thus
      grieved as I ?
But who comes here ?

[*Enter* LUCENTIO *and* PETRUCHIO, *with the* Tutor, *who
60   carries a lute and books.*]

                    God save you, gentlemen !
    Pet. [*bowing*]. And you, good sir ! Pray, have you
    not a daughter

---

41. *Hilding*, Mean-spirited wretch.
53. *Lead apes in hell*, The destiny of the spinster after death.

Call'd Katharina, fair and virtuous ?

 Bap. [*guardedly*]. I have a daughter, sir, called
  Katharina.

 Luc. [*aside to* PETRUCHIO]. You are too blunt : go
  to it orderly.

 Pet. You wrong me, friend Lucentio ; give me leave.

70 I am a gentleman of Verona, sir,

That, hearing of her beauty and her wit,

Her affability and bashful modesty,

Her wondrous qualities and mild behaviour,

Am bold to show myself a forward guest

Within your house, to make mine eye the witness

Of that report which I so oft have heard.

And, for an entrance to my entertainment,

I do present you with a man of mine,

  [*Presenting the* Tutor, *who has laid down the lute
80   and books.*

Cunning in music and the mathematics,

To instruct her fully in these sciences,

Whereof I know she is not ignorant :

Accept of him, or else you do me wrong.

 Bap. You're welcome, sir ; and he, for your good
  sake.

But for my daughter Katharine, this I know,

She is not for your turn, the more my grief.

 Pet. I see you do not mean to part with her,

90 Or else you like not of my company.

 Bap. Mistake me not ; I speak but as I find.

Whence are you, sir ? what may I call your name ?

 Pet. Petruchio is my name ; Antonio's son,

A man well known throughout all Italy.

 Bap. I know him well : you are welcome for his
  sake.

 Luc. Saving your tale, Petruchio, I pray,

Let me, a poor petitioner, speak too.

[*To* BAPTISTA] Pardon me, sir, the boldness is mine
100 own,

That being a stranger in this city here,

Do make myself a suitor to your daughter,
Unto Bianca, fair and virtuous.
Nor is your firm resolve unknown to me,
In the preferment of the eldest sister.
This liberty is all that I request,
That, upon knowledge of my parentage,
I may have welcome 'mongst the rest that woo.
And, toward the education of your daughters,
110 I here bestow a simple instrument,
And this small packet of Greek and Latin books :
If you accept them, then their worth is great.
    [*The* Tutor *brings forward the lute and the books.*
 Bap. I thank you, sir. Your name and parentage ?
 Luc. Lucentio is my name, son to Vincentio.
 Bap. A mighty man of Pisa ; by report
I know him well : you are very welcome, sir.
[*To the* Tutor] Take you the lute, sir, and the set of
  books,
120 You shall go see your pupils presently.
Holla, within !

      [*Enter a* Servant.]

     Sirrah, lead this gentleman
To my daughters ; and tell them both,
This is their tutor : bid them use him well.
      [*Exit* Servant *with the* Tutor.
We will go walk a little in the orchard,
And then to dinner. You are passing welcome,
And so I pray you both to think yourselves.
130 *Pet.* Signior Baptista, my business asketh haste,
And every day I cannot come to woo.
You knew my father well, and in him me,
Left solely heir to all his lands and goods,
Which I have better'd rather than decreased :
Then tell me, if I get your daughter's love,
What dowry shall I have with her to wife ?

120. *Presently*, At once.

Bap. After my death the one half of my lands,
And in possession twenty thousand crowns.

Pet. And, for that dowry, I'll assure her of
140 Her widowhood, be it that she survive me,
In all my lands and leases whatsoever :
Let specialties be therefore drawn between us,
That covenants may be kept on either hand.

Bap. [*doubtfully*]. Ay, when the special thing is
    well obtain'd,
That is, her love ; for that is all in all.

Pet. Why, that is nothing ; for I tell you, father,
I am as peremptory as she proud-minded ;
And where two raging fires meet together
150 They do consume the thing that feeds their fury :
Though little fire grows great with little wind,
Yet extreme gusts will blow out fire and all :
So I to her and so she yields to me :
For I am rough and woo not like a babe.

Bap. Well mayst thou woo, and happy be thy speed !
But be thou arm'd for some unhappy words.

[*Enter the* Tutor, *looking pale and dishevelled, a bruise
    on his forehead, his head protruding through his
    lute, which is round his neck like a collar.*]

160 How now, my friend ! why dost thou look so pale ?

Tutor. For fear, I promise you, if I look pale.

Bap. What, will my daughter prove a good
    musician ?

Tutor. I think she'll sooner prove a soldier :
Iron may hold with her, but never lutes.

Bap. Why, then thou canst not break her to the
    lute ?

Tutor. Why, no ; for she hath broke the lute to me.
I did but tell her she mistook her frets,

---

142. *Specialties*, The articles of a contract.
169. *Frets*, Pieces of wire fastened on the lute to guide the movement
    of the fingers.

170 And bow'd her hand to teach her fingering ;
When, with a most impatient devilish spirit,
" Frets, call you these ? " quoth she ; " I'll fume with
   them : "
And, with that word, she struck me on the head,
And through the instrument my pate made way ;
And there I stood amazed for a while,
As on a pillory, looking through this lute :
While she did call me rascal fiddler
And twangling Jack ; with twenty such vile terms,
180 As had she studied to misuse me so.

Pet. [*with a gesture of appreciation*]. Now, by the
   world, it is a lusty wench ;
I love her ten times more than e'er I did :
O, how I long to have some chat with her !

Bap. [*to the* Tutor]. Well, go with me and be not so
   discomfited :
Proceed in practice with my younger daughter ;
She's apt to learn and thankful for good turns.
Signior Petruchio, will you go with us,
190 Or shall I send my daughter Kate to you ?

Pet. [*with great enthusiasm*]. I pray you do.
                    [*Exeunt all but* PETRUCHIO.
                         I will attend her here,
And woo her with some spirit when she comes.
Say that she rail ; why then I'll tell her plain
She sings as sweetly as a nightingale ;
Say that she frown ; I'll say she looks as clear
As morning roses newly washed with dew :
Say she be mute and will not speak a word ;
200 Then I'll commend her volubility,
And say she uttereth piercing eloquence :
If she do bid me pack, I'll give her thanks,
As though she bid me stay by her a week :
If she deny to wed, I'll crave the day
When I shall ask the banns and when be married.
But here she comes ; and now, Petruchio, speak.

[*Enter* KATHARINA. *He swaggers up to her, and bows to her with a sweeping gesture.*]

Good morrow, Kate ; for that's your name, I hear.
210   *Kath.* [*witheringly*]. Well have you heard, but some-
       thing hard of hearing :
They call me Katharine that do talk of me.
     Pet. You lie, in faith ; for you are call'd plain
       Kate,
And bonny Kate and sometimes Kate the curst ;
But Kate, the prettiest Kate in Christendom,
Kate of Kate Hall, my super-dainty Kate,
For dainties are all Kates, and therefore, Kate,
Take this of me, Kate of my consolation ;
220 Hearing thy mildness praised in every town,
Thy virtues spoke of, and thy beauty sounded,
Yet not so deeply as to thee belongs,
Myself am moved to woo thee for my wife.
     Kath. Moved ! in good time : let him that moved
       you hither
Remove you hence.
     Pet. [*laughingly, taking her hands*]. Come, come, you
       wasp : i' faith, you are too angry.
     Kath. If I be waspish, best beware my sting.
230   [*She strikes him.*
     Pet. I swear I'll cuff you, if you strike again.
     Kath. If you strike me, you are no gentleman.
I chafe you, if I tarry : let me go.
     [*She wrenches herself free and makes for the door,
       but* PETRUCHIO *is there before her. She crosses
       the stage as if to go out by another door, but
       again he forestalls her. She makes another
       attempt as if for the first door, and is once more
       frustrated. This goes on while they speak the
240   next few speeches.*

     215. *Curst*, Bad tempered.
     218. *All Kates*, Punning on *cates :* dainty food.

Pet. No, not a whit ; I find you passing gentle.
[*Indignantly*] 'Twas told me you were rough and coy
    and sullen,
And now I find report a very liar ;
[*Raptly*] For thou art pleasant, gamesome, passing
    courteous,
But slow in speech, yet sweet as springtime flowers :
Thou canst not frown, thou canst not look askance,
Nor bite the lip, as angry wenches will,
250 Why doth the world report that Kate doth limp ?
O slanderous world ! Kate like the hazel-twig
Is straight and slender and as brown·in hue
As hazel nuts and sweeter than the kernels,
O, let me see thee walk : thou dost not halt.
    Kath. Go, fool, and whom thou keep'st command.
    Pet. [*with exaggerated rapture*]. Did ever Dian so be-
        come a grove
As Kate this chamber with her princely gait ?
[*In his usual tone of voice*] Sweet Katharine, your
260   father hath consented
That you shall be my wife ; your dowry 'greed on ;
And will you, nill you, I will marry you.
        [*Takes her in his arms and gives her a resounding
        kiss. She struggles and pushes him away.*
Here comes your father : never make denial ;
I must and will have Katharine to my wife.

[*Enter* BAPTISTA, *with* LUCENTIO *and* BIANCA, *who
    appear well pleased with one another.*]

    Bap. Now, Signior Petruchio, how speed you with
270   my daughter ?
    Pet. [*in pretended surprise*]. How but well, sir, how
        but well ?
It were impossible I should speed amiss.

---

256. *Dian*, Diana, the goddess of hunting and the moon.
262. *Nill*, Will not.
269. *How speed you*, How succeed you ; how did you get on ?
    (2,799)   4

Bap. Why, how now, daughter Katharine! in
    your dumps?

Kath. [*in a voice trembling with anger*]. Call you me
    daughter now, I promise you
You have show'd a tender fatherly regard,
To wish me wed to one half lunatic;
280 A mad-cap ruffian and a swearing Jack,
That thinks with oaths to face the matter out.

Pet. Father, 'tis thus: yourself and all the world,
That talk'd of her, have talked amiss of her:
She is not curst: we have 'greed so well together,
That upon Sunday is the wedding day.

Kath. [*astounded and furious*]. I'll see thee hang'd
    on Sunday first.

Luc. Hark, Petruchio; she says she'll see thee
    hanged first.

290 *Pet.* I tell you, 'tis incredible to believe
How much she loves me: O, the kindest Kate!
She hung about my neck; and kiss on kiss
She vied so fast, protesting oath on oath,
That in a twink she won me to her love.
Give me thy hand, Kate [*She puts her hands behind her
    back*]: I will unto Venice,
To buy apparel 'gainst the wedding day.
Provide the feast, father, and bid the guests,
I will be sure my Katharine shall be fine.

300 *Bap.* I know what to say: but give me your hands;
                    [*He joins their hands together.*
God send you joy, Petruchio! 'tis a match.

Pet. [*delightedly*]. I will to Venice; Sunday comes
    apace:
We will have rings and things and fine array:
And kiss me, Kate, we will be married o' Sunday.
    [*He tries to kiss her, but she slips under his arm and
        goes out angrily.*

CURTAIN

SCENE II

A room in BAPTISTA'S *house.* KATHARINA *sits alone.*

[*Enter* BAPTISTA, HORTENSIO, ROSINA, LUCENTIO, BIANCA, Guests, *and* Attendants.]

    Bap. [*to* LUCENTIO]. Signior Lucentio, this is the 'pointed day
That Katharine and Petruchio should be married,
And yet we hear not of our son-in-law.
What will be said ? what mockery will it be,
10 To want the bridegroom when the priest attends
To speak the ceremonial rites of marriage !
What says Lucentio to this shame of ours ?
    Kath. [*bitterly*]. No shame but mine : I must, forsooth, be forced
To give my hand opposed against my heart
Unto a mad-brain rudesby full of spleen ;
Who woo'd in haste and means to wed at leisure.
I told you, I, he was a frantic fool,
Hiding his bitter jests in blunt behaviour :
20 And, to be noted for a merry man,
He'll woo a thousand, 'point the day of marriage,
Make feasts, invite friends, and proclaim the banns ;
Yet never means to wed where he hath woo'd.
Now must the world point at poor Katharine,
And say, " Lo, there is mad Petruchio's wife,
If it would please him come and marry her ! "
    Luc. Patience, good Katharine, and Baptista too.
Upon my life, Petruchio means but well,
Whatever fortune stays him from his word :
30 Though he be blunt, I know him passing wise ;
Though he be merry, yet withal he's honest.

16. *Rudesby,* Rude boor.   16. *Spleen,* Caprice.

Kath. Would Katharine had never seen him though!
[*Exit weeping, followed by* BIANCA.
Bap. [*much troubled*]. Go, girl; I cannot blame
thee now to weep;
For such an injury would vex a very saint,
Much more a shrew of thy impatient humour.

[*Enter* BIONDELLO, *in great excitement.*]

Bion. Master, master! news, old news, and such
40   news as you never heard of!
Bap. Is it new and old too? how may that be?
Bion. Why, is it not news, to hear of Petruchio's
coming?
Bap. [*much relieved*]. Is he come?
Bion. Why, no, sir.
Bap. What then?
Bion. He is coming.
Bap. When will he be here?
Bion. When he stands where I am and sees you
50   there.
Hor. But say, what to thine old news?
Bion. [*scandalized, but relishing the situation*]. Why,
Petruchio is coming in a new hat and an old jerkin, a
pair of old breeches thrice turned, a pair of boots that
have been candle-cases, one buckled, another laced, an
old rusty sword ta'en out of the town-armoury, with
a broken hilt, and chapeless; with two broken points:
his horse hipped, with an old mothy saddle and
stirrups of no kindred.
60   *Bap.* Who comes with him?
Bion. O, sir, his lackey, for all the world caparisoned
like the horse; with a linen stock on one leg and a
kersey boot-hose on the other, gartered with a red and

57. *Chapeless*, Without a chape, or metal end to the scabbard.
58. *Hipped*, Galled in the hips.
62. *Stock*, Stocking.   63. *Kersey*, Coarse woollen cloth.
63. *Boot hose*, Stockings to be worn with boots.

blue list: a monster, a very monster in apparel, and
not like a Christian footboy or a gentleman's lackey.

Luc. 'Tis some odd humour pricks him to this
fashion.

Bap. I am glad he's come, howso'er he comes.

Bion. Why, sir, he comes not.

70 *Bap.* [*exasperated*]. Didst thou not say he comes?

Bion. [*as if at a loss*]. Who? that Petruchio came?

Bap. Ay, [*very distinctly*] that Petruchio came.

Bion. No, sir; I say his horse comes, with him on
his back.

Bap. [*impatiently*]. Why, that's all one.

[*Enter* PETRUCHIO *and his servant* GRUMIO. *Their
appearance is as* BIONDELLO *has described it.*
PETRUCHIO *is in the wildest good spirits.*]

Pet. Come, where be these gallants? who's at
80 home?

Bap. [*puzzled, but courteous*]. You are welcome, sir.

Pet. But where is Kate? where is my lovely bride?
How does my father? [*Gazes round in hurt surprise.*]
Gentles, methinks you frown:
And wherefore gaze this goodly company,
As if they saw some wondrous monument,
Some comet or unusual prodigy?

Bap. Why, sir, you know this is your wedding day:
First were we sad, fearing you would not come;
90 Now sadder, that you come so unprovided.
Fie, doff this habit, shame to your estate,
An eyesore to our solemn festival!

Luc. See not your bride in these unreverent robes:
Go to my chamber; put on robes of mine.

Pet. Not I, believe me: thus I'll visit her.

Bap. But thus, I trust, you will not marry her.

Pet. Good sooth, even thus; therefore ha' done
with words:

---

91. *Estate*, Rank.

To me she's married, not unto my clothes :
100 Could I repair what she will wear in me,
As I can change these poor accoutrements,
'Twere well for Kate and better for myself.
But what a fool I am to chat with you,
When I should bid good morrow to my bride,
And seal the title with a lovely kiss !

>   [*He strides out followed by* GRUMIO.

   Luc. He hath some meaning in his mad attire.
   Bap. We'll after him, and see the event of this.

> 110   [*All go out. Music, suitable for the rite of the
>   marriage service, is heard. There is a short
>   silence ; then more music. If it is desirable to
>   introduce pageantry, those present at the wed-
>   ding may re-enter in procession, heralded by
>   minstrels and children bearing baskets of rose-
>   mary and garlands of gilded wheat. There
>   may be a dance, and the dancers are suddenly
>   scattered by* PETRUCHIO *striding into their
>   midst, and signing to the musicians to cease
>   playing.*

120   *Pet.* Gentlemen and friends, I thank you for your
      pains :
I know you think to dine with me to-day,
And have prepared great store of wedding cheer :
But so it is, my haste doth call me hence,
And therefore here I mean to take your leave.
   Bap. Is't possible you will away to-night ?
   Pet. I must away to-day, before night come :
And, honest company, I thank you all,
That have beheld me give away myself
130 To this most patient, sweet, and virtuous wife :
Dine with my father, drink a health to me ;
For I must hence ; and farewell to you all.
   Luc. Let us entreat you stay till after dinner.
   Pet. It may not be.
   Hor.   Let me entreat you.
   Pet. It cannot be.

Kath. Let *me* entreat you.

Pet. I am content.

Kath. [*suspiciously*]. Are you content to stay ?

140 *Pet.* I am content you shall entreat me stay ;
But yet not stay, entreat me how you can.

Kath. Now, if you love me, stay.

[*Puts her hand on his arm.*

Pet. Grumio, my horse.

Grum. [*bustling up*]. Ay, sir, they be ready ; the
oats have eaten the horses.

Kath. Nay, then,
Do what thou canst, I will not go to-day ;
No, nor to-morrow, not till I please myself.
150 The door is open, sir ; there lies your way ;
You may be jogging whiles your boots are green ;
For me, I'll not be gone till I please myself :
'Tis like you'll prove a jolly surly groom,
That take it on you at the first so roundly.

Pet. [*kissing her hand*]. O Kate, content thee ;
prithee, be not angry.

Kath. I will be angry : what hast thou to do ?
Father, be quiet : he shall stay my leisure.

Luc. [*aside to* BAPTISTA]. Ay, marry, sir, now it
160 begins to work.

Kath. Gentlemen, forward to the bridal dinner :
I see a woman may be made a fool,
If she had not a spirit to resist.

[*The guests stand irresolute, looking from one to the
other.*

Pet. They shall go forward, Kate, at thy command.
Obey the bride, you that attend on her ;
Go to the feast, revel and domineer,
Carouse full measure to her maidenhead,
170 Be mad and merry, or go hang yourselves :
But for my bonny Kate, she must with me.
Nay, look not big, nor stamp, nor stare, nor fret ;
I will be master of what is mine own,
And here she stands, touch her whoever dare ;

I'll bring my action on the proudest he
That stops my way in Padua.   [*Draws his sword and
        strikes an attitude*] Grumio,
Draw forth thy weapon, we are beset with thieves ;
Rescue thy mistress, if thou be a man.
180 Fear not, sweet wench, they shall not touch thee,
        Kate ;
I'll buckler thee against a million.

> [*With one hand he urges* KATE *out, with the other
>   flourishing his ancient sword as if to protect her
>   from the gazing guests.*

Bap. [*half amused, half angry*]. Nay, let them go,
a couple of quiet ones.

Hor. Went they not quickly, I should die with
        laughing.

190 *Bap.* [*shaking his head*]. Of all mad matches never
        was the like.

Luc. Mistress, what's your opinion of your sister ?

Bian. That, being mad herself, she's madly mated.

Bap. Neighbours and friends, though bride and
        bridegroom wants
For to supply the places at the table,
You know there wants no junkets at the feast.
Lucentio, you shall supply the bridegroom's place ;
And let Bianca take her sister's room.

200 *Luc.* [*taking her by the hand*]. Shall sweet Bianca
        practise how to bride it ?

Bap. She shall, Lucentio.   Come, gentlemen, let's
        go.   [*They go out to music.*

CURTAIN

197. *Junkets*, Sweetmeats.

SCENE III

A room, bare and cold-looking, in PETRUCHIO'S
country house.   A table is half laid.

[*Enter* GRUMIO, *walking as if he were miserably
stiff and tired.*]

Gru. Fie, fie on all tired jades, on all mad masters,
and all foul ways !   Was ever man so beaten ?   was
ever man so rayed ?   was ever man so weary ?   I am
sent before to make a fire, and they are coming after to
10 warm them. [*Shivers, with teeth chattering.*] Now, were
I not a little pot and soon hot, my very lips might
freeze to my teeth, my tongue to the roof of my mouth,
ere I should come by a fire to thaw me : but I, with
blowing the fire, shall warm myself ; for, considering
the weather, a taller man than I will take cold.

[*Enter four or five* Serving-men, *who cluster round*
GRUMIO *in great excitement.*]

Nathaniel. Welcome home, Grumio !

                          [*Takes one hand.*
20   *Philip.* How now, Grumio !   [*Pats his shoulder.*
   Joseph. What, Grumio !   [*Takes the other hand.*
   Nicholas. Fellow Grumio !   [*Smacks his back.*
   Nath. How now, old lad ?

                  [*Shaking his hand violently.*
   Gru. [*dealing with them with great alacrity*]. Welcome, you ;—how now, you ;—what, you ;—fellow,
you ;—and thus much for greeting. [*Folds his arms
and eyes them.*] Now, my spruce companions, is all
ready, and all things neat ?
30   *Nath.* All things is ready.   How near is our master ?

---

8. *Rayed*, May mean befouled, or stand for *arrayed* (beset), or
     arrayed (dressed).

Gru. E'en at hand, alighted by this ; and therefore
be not—Cock's passion, silence ! I hear my master.
> [*Footsteps, the cracking of a whip, shouting.*

[*Enter* PETRUCHIO, *striding and swaggering, and* KATH-
ARINA, *muffled in a long dark cloak, drooping,
and already subdued.*]

Pet. [*fuming*]. Where be these knaves ? What, no
man at door
To hold my stirrup nor to take my horse ?
40 [*Shouting*] Where is Nathaniel—Gregory—Philip ?
Servants [*in great trepidation*]. Here, here, sir ;
here, sir.
Pet. [*mocking them angrily*]. Here, sir ! here, sir !
here, sir ! here, sir !
You logger-headed and unpolished grooms !
What, no attendance ? no regard ? no duty ?
[*Glaring round*] Where is the foolish knave I sent
before ?
Gru. [*cheerfully*]. Here, sir, as foolish as I was be-
50   fore.
Pet. Did I not bid thee meet me in the park,
And bring along these rascal knaves with thee ?
Gru. [*explaining with politeness and complete self-
possession*]. Nathaniel's coat, sir, was not fully
made ;
And Gabriel's pumps were all unpink'd i' the heel ;
There was no link to colour Peter's hat ;
And Walter's dagger was not come from sheathing :
There were none fine but Adam, Ralph, and Gregory ;
60 The rest were ragged, old, and beggarly ;
Yet, as they are [*with a grand gesture*] here are they
come to meet you.
Pet. Go, rascals, go, and fetch my supper in.
> [*The* Servants *bustle out, tumbling over one another
in their hurry to be gone.*

32. *Cock,* For God.
56. *Unpink'd,* Not " pinked," or pierced with eyelet-holes.

Pet. [*singing*].

* Where is the life that late I led?

Where are those—Sit down, Kate, and welcome.

[*The* Servants *bring in supper.*

70 Why, when, I say? Nay, good sweet Kate, be merry.
Off with my boots, you rogues, you villains, when?

[*A* Servant *begins to pull off his boots.*

[*Singing*].

† It was a friar of ord-ers grey (*Hums tune* . . . . .

. . . .) As he forth walk-ed on his way . . .

(*Hums tune* . . . .)

Out, you rogue, you pluck my foot awry:
Take that, and mend the plucking of the other.

[*Strikes him.*

80 Be merry, Kate. Some water, here; what, ho!
Where's my spaniel Troilus? Sirrah, get you hence—

* The tune is "With a fading."
† The tune is "And how should I your true love know."

Where are my slippers ?   Shall I have some water ?

[*Enter a* Servant *with water and a towel*.]

Pet. Come, Kate, and wash, and welcome heartily.
[*To the* Servant] You plaguey villain, will you let it
          fall ?   [*Strikes him.*
    Kath. Patience, I pray you ; 'twas a fault unwilling.
    Pet. A plaguey beetle-headed, flap-ear'd knave !
Come, Kate, sit down ; I know you have a stomach.
90   [*They seat themselves at opposite ends of the table,*
            KATHARINA *shivering, sullen, and unhappy.*
Will you give thanks, sweet Kate, or else shall I ?
            [*Uncovering a dish, and gazing at it in distaste.*
What's this ? mutton ?
    Nath. Ay.
    Pet.   Who brought it ?
    Peter.   I.
    Pet. 'Tis burnt ; and so is all the meat.
What dogs are these !   Where is the rascal cook ?
100 How durst you, villains, bring it from the dresser,
And serve it thus to me that love it not ?
There, take it to you, trenchers, cups, and all :
                    [*Throws the meat, etc., about the stage.*
You heedless joltheads and unmannered slaves !
What, do you grumble ?   I'll be with you straight.
      [*Threatens the servants, who scurry out as quickly
          as may be.*
    Kath. I pray you, husband, be not so disquiet :
The meat was well, if you were so contented.
110   *Pet.* I tell thee, Kate, 'twas burnt and dried away ;
And I expressly am forbid to touch it,
For it engenders choler, planteth anger ;
And better 'twere that both of us did fast,
Since, of ourselves, ourselves are choleric,
Than feed it with such over-roasted flesh.
Be patient ; to-morrow 't shall be mended,
And for this night, we'll fast for company :
Come, I will bring thee to thy bridal chamber.

[*They go out,* KATHARINA *with a longing and rueful*
120 *glance at the broken pieces of food on the floor.*
The Servants *steal in, one by one, looking*
cautiously about as if they feared to encounter
their master.

Nath. Peter, didst ever see the like ?

Peter. He kills her in her own humour.

Gru. Where is he ?

Curtis. Making a sermon of the good wife to her,
And rails, and swears, and rates, that she, poor soul,
Knows not which way to stand, to look, to speak,
130 And sits as one new-risen from a dream.
Away, away ! for he is coming hither.

[*They scuttle off in mortal terror.* PETRUCHIO
comes in, and, seating himself on the table, arms
folded, looks round at the débris of the feast.

Pet. This is a way to kill a wife with kindness ;
And thus I'll curb her mad and headstrong humour.
He that knows better how to tame a shrew,
Now let him speak : 'tis charity to show.

CURTAIN

SCENE IV

As in Scene III. KATHARINA *sits at the table, her chin*
propped on her hands, looking cold and miserable.

[*Enter* PETRUCHIO *and* HORTENSIO, *followed by*
GRUMIO, *carrying a covered dish.*]

Pet. [*with exaggerated concern*]. How fares my Kate ?
What, sweeting, all amort ?

Hor. [*bowing and kissing her hand*]. Mistress, what
cheer ?

10 *Kath.* [*shivering, too miserable to welcome him*]. Faith,
as cold as can be.

7. *Amort,* Dejected.

Pet. Pluck up thy spirits ; look cheerfully upon me.
Here, love ; thou see'st how diligent I am
To dress thy meat myself and bring it thee :
I am sure, sweet Kate, this kindness merits thanks.

> [GRUMIO *uncovers the dish, which he has set on the
> table.* KATHARINA *sits with head turned from
> her husband ; her attitude suggesting that she
> will never speak to him again.*

20 What, not a word ?   Nay, then thou lovest it not ;
And all my pains is sorted to no proof.
[*To* GRUMIO] Here, take away this dish.

Kath. [*seizing it with both hands*]. I pray you, let it
stand.

Pet. The poorest service is repaid with thanks ;
And so shall mine, before you touch the meat.

Kath. I thank you, sir.

Hor. Signior Petruchio, fie ! you are to blame.
Come, Mistress Kate, I'll bear you company.

30   [*Sits down at the table beside her.*

Pet. [*aside*]. Eat it all up, Hortensio, if thou lovest
me.

> [*The two begin the meal,* KATHARINA *eating raven-
> ously.* PETRUCHIO *looks on benignly.*

Much good it do unto thy gentle heart !
Kate, eat apace : and now, my honey love,
Will we return unto thy father's house
And revel it as bravely as the best,
With silken coats and caps and golden rings,
40 With ruffs and cuffs and fardingales and things ;
With scarfs and fans and double change of bravery,
With amber bracelets, beads, and all this knavery.
What, hast thou dined ?   The tailor stays thy leisure,
To deck thy body with his ruffling treasure.

> [*Enter* Tailor, *an obsequious little fellow, carrying a
> gown and a measure.*]

Come, tailor, let us see these ornaments ;
Lay forth the gown.

[Enter Haberdasher, *carrying a round silken cap.]*

50   What news with you, sir ?

Hab. Here is the cap your worship did bespeak.

  [Holds it out. KATHARINA *gets up from the table to
  take it from him, her expression one of lively
  interest, but* PETRUCHIO *is too quick for her.*

 Pet. [holding up the cap and regarding it with scorn].
Why, this was moulded on a porringer !
A velvet dish : fie, fie ! a loathsome trifle :
Why, 'tis a cockle or a walnut-shell,
A knack, a toy, a trick, a baby's cap :
60 Away with it ! come, let me have a bigger.

 Kath. [determinedly]. I'll have no bigger : this doth
  fit the time,
And gentlewomen wear such caps as these.

 Pet. [giving it to the Haberdasher]. When you are
  gentle, you shall have one too,
And not till then.

 Kath. Why, sir, I trust I may have leave to speak ;
And speak I will ; I am no child, no babe :
Your betters have endured me say my mind,
70 And if you cannot, best you stop your ears.

 Pet. [as if delighted with her good sense]. Why, thou
  say'st true : it is a paltry cap.
A custard-coffin, a bauble, a silken pie :
I love thee well, in that thou likest it not.

 Kath. Love me or love me not, I like the cap ;
And it I will have, or I will have none.

  [Crosses to the Haberdasher, *who is about to give it
  to her, but, at a threatening sign from* PETRU-
  CHIO, *goes out in haste.*

80 *Pet. [as if she had asked for it].* Thy gown ? why,
  ay : come, tailor, let us see't.

 [In amazement and disgust] O mercy, God ! what
  masquing stuff is here ?

---

73. *Custard-coffin,* The crust of a custard pie.

What's this ? a sleeve ? 'tis like a demi-cannon :
What, up and down, carved like an apple-tart ?
Here's snip and nip and cut and slish and slash,
Like to a censer in a barber's shop :
Why, what i' devil's name, tailor, call'st thou this ?

  Tai. [*remonstrating*]. You bid me make it orderly
90   and well,
According to the fashion and the time.

  Pet. [*sharply*]. Marry, and did ; but if you be re-
   member'd,
I did not bid you mar it to the time.
Go, hop me over every kennel home,
For you shall hop without my custom, sir :
I'll none of it : hence ! make your best of it.
   [*The* Tailor *stands in an attitude of expostulation,
   the gown over one arm.*

100 *Kath.* [*indignantly*]. I never saw a better-fashion'd
   gown,
More quaint, more pleasing, nor more commendable :
Belike you mean to make a puppet of me.

  Pet. [*sympathetically*]. Why, true ; he means to
   make a puppet of thee.

  Tai. [*obsequious but annoyed*]. She says your worship means to make a puppet of her.

  Pet. [*as if infuriated*]. O monstrous arrogance ! Thou
   liest, thou thread, thou thimble.
110 Thou yard, three-quarters, half-yard, quarter, nail !
Thou flea, thou nit, thou winter-cricket thou !
[*Outraged at the notion*] Braved in mine own house
   with a skein of thread !
Away, thou rag, thou quantity, thou remnant ;
Or I shall so be-mete thee with thy yard
As thou shalt think on prating whilst thou livest !
I tell thee, I, that thou hast marr'd her gown.

  Tai. [*in a small voice, but upholding his side of the*

---

87. *Censer,* Used for burning perfumes. 95. *Kennel,* Gutter.
114. *Quantity,* Small portion of anything. 115. *Be-mete,* Measure.

120 *case*]. Your worship is deceived ; the gown is made
Just as my master had direction :
Grumio gave order how it should be done.

    Gru. I gave him no order ; I gave him the stuff.

    Tai. But how did you desire it should be made ?

    Gru. Marry, sir, with needle and thread.

    Tai. But did you not request to have it cut ?

    Gru. [*taking him by the shoulder and looking him in the eye*]. Thou hast faced many things.

    Tai. [*proudly*]. I have.

130   *Gru.* Face not me : thou hast braved many men ; brave not me ; I will be neither faced nor braved. I say unto thee, I bid thy master cut out the gown ; but I did not bid him cut it to pieces : ergo, thou liest.

    Tai. [*producing a paper*]. Why, here is the note of the fashion to testify.

    Pet. Read it.

    Tai. [*reads*]. " Imprimis, a loose-bodied gown."

    Gru. I said, a gown.

    Pet. Proceed.

140   *Tai.* [*reads*]. " With a small compassed cape."

    Gru. I confess the cape.

    Tai. [*reads*]. " With a trunk sleeve : "

    Gru. I confess two sleeves.

    Tai. [*reads*]. " The sleeves curiously cut."

    Pet. Ay, there's the villainy.

    Gru. [*airily*]. Error i' the bill, sir ; error i' the bill. I commanded the sleeves should be cut out and sewed up again ; and that I'll prove upon thee, though thy little finger be armed in a thimble.

150   [*Threatens the* Tailor.

    Tai. [*with rather ineffective indignation*]. This is true that I say : an I had thee in place where, thou shouldst know it.

---

130. *Braved*, Made brave, or fine.   133. *Ergo*, Therefore.
140. *Compassed*, Arched, round.   144. *Curiously*, Fancifully.

Gru. I am for thee straight : take thou the bill [*hands him the paper*], give me thy mete-yard, and spare not me.   [*Strikes an attitude.*

Pet. [*aside*]. Hortensio, say thou wilt see the tailor paid.

[*To* Tailor] Go take it hence ; be gone, and say no
160 more.

Hor. Tailor, I'll pay thee for thy gown to-morrow :
Take no unkindness of his hasty words :
Away ! I say ; commend me to thy master.

[*Somewhat mollified, though still bewildered and irritated, the* Tailor *goes out.*

Pet. Well, come, my Kate ; we will unto your father's,
Even in these honest mean habiliments :
[*Preaching*] Our purses shall be proud, our garments
170 poor ;
For 'tis the mind that makes the body rich ;
And as the sun breaks through the darkest clouds,
So honour peereth in the meanest habit.
What, is the jay more precious than the lark,
Because his feathers are more beautiful ?
Or is the adder better than the eel,
Because his painted skin contents the eye ?
O, no, good Kate ; neither art thou the worse
For this poor furniture and mean array.
180 If thou account'st it shame, lay it on me ;
And therefore frolic : we will hence forthwith,
To feast and sport us at thy father's house.
[*To* GRUMIO] Go, call my men, and let us straight to him ;
And bring our horses unto Long-lane end ;
There will we mount, and thither walk on foot.
Let's see ; I think 'tis now some seven o'clock,
And well we may come there by dinner-time.

Kath. I dare assure you, sir, 'tis almost two ;
And 'twill be supper-time ere you come there.

190 *Pet.* It shall be seven ere I go to horse :
[*Hurt*] Look, what I speak, or do, or think to do,

You are still crossing it. Sirs, let 't alone :
I will not go to-day ; and ere I do,
It shall be what o'clock I say it is.

> [*Flings himself down in a chair.* KATHARINA
> *stares at him hopelessly.*

    Hor. [*aside*]. Why, so this gallant will command the
sun.   [*Gazes at him in consternation.*

CURTAIN

SCENE V

BAPTISTA'S *house.* BAPTISTA, PETRUCHIO, LU-
CENTIO, *and* HORTENSIO *are drinking at a table, left of
the stage.* BIONDELLO *fills their wine-cups.*

    Bap. You talk of wives :
Now, in good sadness, son Petruchio,
I think thou hast the veriest shrew of all.
    Pet. Well, I say no : and therefore for assurance
Let's each one send unto his wife ;
10 And he whose wife is most obedient
To come at first when he doth send for her,
Shall win the wager which we will propose.
    Hor. [*eagerly*]. Content. What is the wager ?
    Luc. [*with the confidence of the sure winner*]. Twenty
crowns.
    Pet. [*scornfully*]. Twenty crowns !
I'll venture so much of my hawk or hound,
But twenty times so much upon my wife.
    Luc. A hundred then.
20   *Hor.*   Content.
    Pet.   A match ! 'tis done.
    Hor. Who shall begin ?
    Luc.   That will I.
Go, Biondello, bid thy mistress come to me.
    Bion. I go.   [*Exit.*

Bap. Son, I'll be your half, Bianca comes.
Luc. I'll have no halves, I'll bear it all myself.

[*Re-enter* BIONDELLO, *alone.*]

How now, what news ?
30 *Bion.*   Sir, my mistress sends you word
That she is busy and she cannot come.
    Pet. [*repeating the words slowly and critically*]. That
        she is busy and she cannot come !
Is that an answer ?
    Hor. [*delighted*]. Ay, and a kind one too :
Pray God, sir, your wife send you not a worse.
    Pet. I hope, better.
    Hor. Sirrah Biondello, go and entreat my wife
To come to me forthwith.   [*Exit* BIONDELLO.
40 *Pet.*   O ho ! entreat her !
Nay, then she must needs come.
    Hor.   I am afraid, sir,
Do what you can, yours will not be entreated.

[*Re-enter* BIONDELLO, *alone.*]

Now, where's my wife ?
    Bion. She says you have some goodly jest in hand :
She will not come ; she bids you come to her.
    Pet. Worse and worse ; she will not come ! O vile,
Intolerable, not to be endured !
50 Sirrah Grumio, go to your mistress ;
Say, I command her come to me.   [*Exit* GRUMIO.
    Hor. I know her answer.
    Pet.   What ?
    Hor.   She will not.
    Pet. [*tranquilly*]. The fouler fortune mine, and there
        an end.
    Bap. [*in utter amazement*]. Now, by my holidame,
        here comes Katharina !

---

57. *Holidame,* For halidom, holiness.

[Enter KATHARINA.]

60   *Kath.* What is your will, sir, that you send for me ?
  Pet. Where is your sister, and Hortensio's wife ?
  Kath. They sit conferring by the parlour fire.
  Pet. Go, fetch them hither : if they deny to come,
Swinge me them soundly forth unto their husbands :
Away, I say, and bring them hither straight.
                              [Exit KATHARINA.
  Luc. Here is a wonder, if you talk of a wonder.
  Hor. And so it is : I wonder what it bodes.
  Pet. Marry, peace it bodes, and love and quiet life,
70 And awful rule and right supremacy ;
And, to be short, what not, that's sweet and happy ?
  Bap. [*clapping him on the shoulder*]. Now, fair
      befall thee, good Petruchio !
The wager thou hast won ; and I will add
Unto their losses twenty thousand crowns ;
Another dowry to another daughter,
For she is changed, as she had never been.
  Pet. Nay, I will win my wager better yet
And show more sign of her obedience,
80 Her new-built virtue and obedience.
See where she comes and brings your froward wives
As prisoners to her womanly persuasion.

[Enter KATHARINA, *with* BIANCA *and* ROSINA.]

Katharine, that cap of yours becomes you not :
Off with that bauble, throw it underfoot.
      [KATHARINA *takes it off and flings it on the ground.*
  Ros. Lord, never let me have a cause to sigh.
Till I be brought to such a silly pass !
  Bian. Fie ! what a foolish duty call you this ?
90   *Luc.* I would your duty were as foolish too :
The wisdom of your duty, fair Bianca,

64. *Swinge,* Beat.

Hath cost me an hundred crowns since supper-time.

   Bian. The more fool you, for laying on my duty.

   Pet. [*with whimsical gravity*]. Katharine, I charge
     thee, tell these headstrong women

What duty they do owe their lords and husbands.

   Ros. Come, come, you're mocking : we will have no
     telling.

   Pet. Come on, I say ; and first begin with her.

100   *Ros.* She shall not.

   Pet. I say she shall ; and first begin with her.

   Kath. [*with gentle sweetness, taking* ROSINA'S *hand*].
     Fie, fie ! unknit that threatening unkind brow,

And dart not scornful glances from those eyes,

To wound thy lord, thy king, thy governor :

It blots thy beauty as frosts do bite the meads,

Confounds thy sense as whirlwinds shake fair buds,

And in no sense is meet or amiable.

A woman moved is like a fountain troubled,

110 Muddy, ill-seeming, thick, bereft of beauty ;

And while it is so, none so dry or thirsty

Will deign to sip or touch one drop of it.

Thy husband is thy lord, thy life, thy keeper,

Thy head, thy sovereign ; one that cares for thee,

And craves no other tribute at thy hands

But love, fair looks, and true obedience.

Come, come, you froward and unable worms !

My mind hath been as big as one of yours,

My heart as great, my reason haply more,

120 To bandy word for word and frown for frown

But now I see our lances are but straws,

Our strength as weak, our weakness past compare,

That seeming to be most which we indeed least are.

   Pet. Why, there's a wench ! Come on, and kiss me,
     Kate.

   Luc. Well, go thy ways, old lad ; for thou shalt ha't.

117. *Unable,* Feeble.
117. *Worms.* Used as " creatures " might be nowadays.

Pet. [*rising*]. 'Twas I won the wager. God give you good-night.

[*He goes out with* KATHARINA. *The others gaze*
130 *after them, in amused astonishment.*

Hor. Now, go thy ways ; thou hast tamed a cursed shrew.

Luc. 'Tis a wonder, by your leave, she will be tamed so.

CURTAIN

THE ADVENTURE ON GADSHILL

(From *Henry IV., Part* 1)

PERSONS OF THE PLAY

HENRY, *Prince of Wales.*
SIR JOHN FALSTAFF, *his boon companion.*
POINS,
GADSHILL, } *four rogues, associates with the Prince and*
PETO, *Falstaff.*
BARDOLPH,
FRANCIS, *a drawer of wine at the Boar's Head Tavern, Eastcheap.*
The Sheriff.
The Travellers.

Situation.—England is on the brink of civil war, but apparently indifferent to the fate which threatens his father's life and crown, the Prince of Wales fritters away his time in idle pleasures. His chief delight is in the humour and humours of that fat old reprobate, Sir John Falstaff, and he consents to join in a plan of highway robbery that he may have the opportunity of playing a practical joke on him.

Time of the story of the play : 1403.
Time occupied in acting the play : an hour.

NOTE ON COSTUME

The most characteristic garment of this time was the houppelande, a loose, high-collared robe, fitting on the shoulders, and cut of a length to suit the wearer. It might reach just below the waist or trail on the ground :

it might be girdled or hang loosely. Sleeves were very
full, ending in a band at the wrist, or cut away to show a
tight under-sleeve, and hanging, with jagged edges, below
the knees. Nearly every man carried sword or dagger.
The head-dress was shaped like an inverted bag, closed
in a band, and turned over to one side; or a soft high-
crowned hat, pulled to a point in front, might be worn.
Travellers wore long cloaks with full sleeves, and peaked
hoods. Colours were splendid, and strong contrasts
were used with gay effect in one costume, the wearing
of hose of two colours being much liked. Francis wears
a tunic of rough durable material in white, russet, or blue.

SCENE I

*A room in the Boar's Head Tavern, Eastcheap. The
walls are hung with arras (tapestry). Left is a settle on
which reposes the enormous form of* FALSTAFF, *and by
it is a table on which stand pewter tankards and flagons.
The rest of the furniture consists of a low bench, and one
or two stools. The floor is strewn with rushes. Half-
sitting on the table near* FALSTAFF, *facing the audience,
is* PRINCE HAL, *a slim dark boy, at the opening of the*
10 *scene impatient and restless in demeanour. He drains a
tankard, sets it down with a bang, folds his arms, and
stares moodily in front of him. Then, his attention
caught by a soft snore from* FALSTAFF, *he jerks round
and regards him, with half-critical amusement. Amusement prevails, and bending down, he picks up a rush
from the floor and tickles the face and head of the sleeper,
who, with a grunt of discomfort, makes one or two in-
effectual attempts to brush away the imaginary fly, and
awakes.*

20   *Fal.* [*drowsily*]. Now, Hal, what time of day is
it, lad?

> [*He stretches out his hand, groping for his tankard,
> which the* PRINCE *adroitly whips out of his
> reach.*

Prince [*petulantly*]. What the plague hast thou to
do with the time of the day ? Unless hours were cups
of sack and minutes capons, I see no reason why thou
shouldst be so superfluous to demand the time of the
day.

30   *Fal.* Indeed, you come near me now, Hal ; for we
that take purses go by the moon and the seven stars,
and not by Phœbus, he [*sings*] " that wandering
knight so fair." And, I prithee, sweet wag, when thou
art king, as God save thy grace—majesty I should say,
for grace thou wilt have none——

Prince. What, none ?

Fal. No, by my troth, not so much as will serve to
be prologue to an egg and butter.

Prince [*half crossly*]. Well, how then ? come,
40 roundly, roundly.

Fal. Marry, then, sweet wag, when thou art king,
let not us that are squires of the night's body be
called thieves of the day's beauty : [*In the tone of one
hunting for a really descriptive complimentary phrase*]
let us be Diana's foresters, gentlemen of the shade,
minions of the moon ; and let men say we be men of
good government, being governed, as the sea is, by
our noble and chaste mistress the moon, under whose
countenance we—steal.

50   *Prince.* Thou sayest well, and it holds well too ; for
the fortune of us that are the moon's men doth ebb
and flow like the sea, being governed, as the sea is, by
the moon. As, for proof, now : a purse of gold most
resolutely snatched on Monday night and most dis-
solutely spent on Tuesday morning ; got with swearing " Lay by " and spent with crying " Bring in " ;
now in as low an ebb as the foot of the ladder and by-
and-by in as high a flow as the ridge of the gallows.

Fal. [*rather uneasily*]. By the Lord, thou sayest

27. *Capons*, Fowl.   40. *Roundly*, Without delay.
46. *Minions*, Favourites.

60 true, lad. [*After a short pause*] But, I prithee, sweet wag, shall there be gallows standing in England when thou art king? and resolution thus fobbed as it is with the rusty curb of old father antic the law? Do not thou, when thou art king, hang a thief.

Prince [*snappishly*]. No; thou shalt.

Fal. Shall I? O rare! By the Lord, I'll be a brave judge.

Prince. Thou judgest false already. I mean, thou shalt have the hanging of the thieves and so become a
70 rare hangman.

Fal. [*making the best of it*]. Well, Hal, well; and in some sort it jumps with my humour as well as waiting in the court, I can tell you. [*With a dignified virtuous air*] But, Hal, I prithee, trouble me no more with vanity. I would to God thou and I knew where a commodity of good names were to be bought. An old lord of the council rated me the other day in the street about you, sir, but I marked him not; and yet he talked very wisely but I regarded him not; and yet
80 he talked wisely, and in the street too.

Prince. Thou didst well; for wisdom cries out in the streets, and no man regards it.

Fal. O thou art indeed able to corrupt a saint. [*Shaking his head*] Thou hast done much harm upon me, Hal; God forgive thee for it! Before I knew thee, Hal, I knew nothing; and now am I, if a man should speak truly, little better than one of the wicked. [*With noble resolution*] I must give over this life, and I will give it over: by the Lord, an I do not, I am
90 a villain; I'll be ruined for never a king's son in Christendom.

Prince [*amused in spite of himself*]. Where shall we take a purse to-morrow, Jack?

Fal. [*delighted at his change of mood*]. Zounds, where

---

63. *Antic*, A grotesque figure.   66. *Brave*, Fine.
72. *Jumps with my humour*, Agrees with my inclination.
76. *Commodity*, Supply.

thou wilt, lad ; I'll make one ; an I do not, call me villain and baffle me.

Prince. I see a good amendment of life in thee ; from praying to purse-taking.

Fal. Why, Hal, 'tis my vocation, Hal ; 'tis no sin
100 for a man to labour in his vocation.

[*Enter* POINS, *a youth straight and slim as* HAL, *but with a sort of vulgar swagger that is in contrast with the bearing of the prince.*]

Poins! Now shall we know if Gadshill have set a match. O, if men were to be saved by merit, what hole in hell were hot enough for him ? This is the most omnipotent villain that ever cried " Stand " to a true man.

Prince. Good-morrow, Ned.

110 *Poins* [*clapping him on the shoulder with exaggerated familiarity*]. Good-morrow, sweet Hal. [*Rallying* FALSTAFF] What says Monsieur Remorse ? what says Sir John Sack and Sugar ? Jack ! how agrees the devil and thee about thy soul, that thou soldest him on Good Friday last for a cup of Madeira and a cold capon's leg ? But, my lads, my lads, to-morrow morning, by four o'clock, early at Gadshill ! there are pilgrims going to Canterbury with rich offerings, and traders riding to London with fat purses : I have
120 vizards for you all ; you have horses for yourselves : Gadshill lies to-night in Rochester : I have bespoke supper to-morrow night in Eastcheap : we may do it as secure as sleep. If you will go, I will stuff your purses full of crowns ; if you will not, tarry at home and be hanged.

Fal. [*who has listened with growing excitement and*

---

96. *Baffle*, Disgrace, a technical term for the punishment of recreant knights.
104. *Set a match*, Made an appointment (to meet with and rob the travellers).   120. *Vizards*, Masks.

enjoyment]. Hear ye, Yedward ; if I tarry at home and go out, I'll hang you for going.

Poins. You will, chops ?

130 *Fal.* Hal, wilt thou make one ?

Prince. Who, I rob ? I a thief ? not I, by my faith.

Fal. There's neither honesty, manhood, nor good fellowship in thee, nor thou camest not of the blood royal, if thou darest not stand for ten shillings.

Prince. Well then, once in my days I'll be a madcap.

Fal. Why, that's well said.

Prince. Well, come what will, I'll tarry at home.

Fal. By the Lord, I'll be a traitor then, when thou
140 art king.

Prince. I care not.

Poins [*aside*]. Sir John, I prithee, leave the prince and me alone : I will lay him down such reasons for this adventure that he shall go.

Fal. Well, God give thee the spirit of persuasion and him the ears of profiting. [*To* HAL] Farewell, good king's son.

Prince. Farewell, thou latter spring ! farewell, All-hallown summer !

150 [FALSTAFF *goes out rather unsteadily,* POINS *takes* HAL'S *arm with an eager gesture.*

Poins. Now, my good sweet honey lord, ride with us to-morrow : I have a jest to execute that I cannot manage alone. Falstaff, Bardolph, Peto, and Gads-hill shall rob those men that we have already waylaid ; yourself and I will not be there ; and when they have the booty, if you and I do not rob them, cut this head off from my shoulders.

Prince. How shall we part with them in setting
160 forth ?

---

129. *Chops*, A person with fat cheeks.
148. *All-hallown summer.* All Hallows or All Saints' Day is the 1st of November. Falstaff is in the autumn of life, but he is gay as a young man in his " summer," or prime.

Poins. Why, we will set forth before or after them, and appoint them a place of meeting, wherein it is at our pleasure to fail ; and then will they adventure upon the exploit themselves ; which they shall have no sooner achieved, but we'll set upon them.

Prince. Yea, but 'tis like that they will know us by our horses, by our habits and by every other appointment, to be ourselves.

Poins [*impatient with so many objections*]. Tut ! our 170 horses they shall not see ; I'll tie them in the wood ; our vizards we will change after we leave them : and, sirrah, I have cases of buckram for the nonce, to inmask our noted outward garments.

Prince. Yea, but I doubt they will be too hard for us.

Poins. Well, for two of them, I know them to be as true-bred cowards as ever turned back ; and for the third, if he fight longer than he sees reason, I'll forswear arms.   The virtue of this jest will be, the incomprehensible lies that this same fat rogue will tell 180 us when we meet at supper : how thirty, at least, he fought with ; what wards, what blows, what extremities he endured ; and in the reproof of this lies the jest.

Prince. Well, I'll go with thee : provide us all things necessary and meet me to-morrow night in Eastcheap, for here I'll sup.   Farewell.

Poins. Farewell, my lord.   [*He goes out.*

Prince [*sitting at the table, and speaking as if in
      reverie*]. I know you all, and will awhile uphold
190 The unyoked humour of your idleness :
Yet herein will I imitate the sun,
Who doth permit the base contagious clouds
To smother up his beauty from the world,
That, when he please again to be himself,
Being wanted, he may be more wondered at,
And like bright metal on a sullen ground,

---

172. *Cases,* Outer garments.   172. *For the nonce.* For the occasion.

My reformation, glittering o'er my fault,
Shall show more goodly and attract more eyes
Than that which hath no foil to set it off.
200 I'll so offend, to make offence a skill ;
Redeeming time when men think least I will.

    [*Props his chin on his clasped hands and remains*
      as if deep in thought.

CURTAIN

SCENE II

The highway near the top of Gadshill.

[*Enter* PRINCE HENRY *and* POINS.]

Poins. Come, shelter, shelter : I have removed
Falstaff's horse, and he frets like a gummed velvet.
  Prince. Stand close.

[*Enter* FALSTAFF, *in the heavy, breathless agitation*
    of a fat man.]

  Fal. Poins ! Poins, and be hanged ! Poins !
10   *Hal* [*rebuking him in a stage whisper*]. Peace, ye
fat-kidneyed rascal ! what a brawling dost thou keep !
  Fal. [*in a husky would-be lowered voice*]. Where's
Poins, Hal ?
  Prince. He is walked up to the top of the hill : I'll
go seek him.   [*He goes out.*
  Fal. I am accursed to rob in that thief's company :
the rascal hath removed my horse, and tied him I
know not where. If I travel but four foot further
afoot, I shall break my wind. Well, I doubt not but
20 to die a fair death for all this, if I 'scape hanging for

---

5. *Gummed velvet*, Velvet stiffened with gum, *i.e.* soon showing
  marks of wear.

killing that rogue. I have forsworn his company
hourly any time this two and twenty years, and yet I
am bewitched with the rogue's company. If the
rascal have not given me medicines to make me love
him I'll be hanged ; it could not be else ; I have drunk
medicines. [*Calling, at first with caution, then loudly
as he can*] Poins ! Hal ! a plague upon you both !
Bardolph ! Peto ! I'll starve ere I rob a foot further.
And 'twere not as good a deed as drink, to turn true
30 man and to leave these rogues, I am the veriest varlet
that ever chewed with a tooth. Eight yards of un-
even ground is threescore and ten miles afoot with
me ; and the stony-hearted villains know it well
enough : a plague upon it when thieves cannot be
true to one another ! [*They whistle.*] Whew ! A
plague upon you all ! Give me my horse, you rogues ;
give me my horse, and be hanged !

[HAL *springs in and puts his hand before his
mouth.*

40 *Prince.* Peace ! lie down ; lay thine ear close to
the ground and list if thou canst hear the tread of
travellers.

Fal. Have you any levers to lift me up again, being
down ? 'Sblood, I'll not bear mine own flesh so far
afoot again for all the coin in thy father's exchequer.
What a plague mean ye to colt me thus ?

Prince. Thou liest ; thou art not colted, thou art
uncolted.

Fal. I prithee, good Prince Hal, help me to my
50 horse, good king's son.

Prince. Out, ye rogue ! shall I be your ostler ?

Fal. Go hang thyself in thine own heir-apparent
garters ! If I be ta'en, I'll peach for this. An I have
not ballads made on you all and sung to filthy tunes,
let a cup of sack be my poison : when a jest is so forward, and afoot too ! I hate it !

---

30. *Varlet*, Contemptuous term, low rascal.   46. *Colt*, Befool.

[*Enter* GADSHILL, BARDOLPH, *and* PETO *with him.*
BARDOLPH *is noticeable on account of the fiery hue
of his complexion.*]

60 *Gads.* Stand.   [*He draws his sword.*

Fal. So I do, against my will.

Poins. O, 'tis our setter; I know his voice. Bardolph, what news?

Bar. [*thickly*]. Case ye, case ye; on with your vizards: there's money of the king's coming down the hill; 'tis going to the king's exchequer.

Fal. You lie, you rogue; 'tis going to the king's tavern.

Gads. There's enough to make us all.

70 *Fal.* To be hanged.

Prince [*quickly making arrangements*]. Sirs, you four shall front them in the narrow lane; Ned Poins and I will walk lower: if they 'scape from your encounter, then they light on us.

Peto. How many be there of them?

Gads. Some eight or ten.

Fal. Zounds, will they not rob us?

Prince. What, a coward, Sir John Paunch?

Fal. [*with dignity*]. Indeed, I am not John of Gaunt,
80 your grandfather; but yet no coward, Hal.

Prince. Well, we leave that to the proof.

Poins. Sirrah Jack, thy horse stands behind the hedge: when thou needst him, there thou shalt find him.   Farewell, and stand fast.

Fal. [*regarding* HAL]. Now cannot I strike him, if I should be hanged.

Prince [*aside*]. Ned, where are our disguises?

Poins [*aside*]. Here, hard by: stand close.

[PRINCE *and* POINS *go out.*

90 *Fal.* [*in high good humour again*]. Now, my masters, happy man be his dole, say I: every man to his business.   [*The sound of horses' hoofs without.*

91. *Dole*, Portion. The saying is an old proverb.

[*Enter the* Travellers.]

First Trav. Come, neighbour ! the boy shall lead our horses down the hill ; we'll walk afoot awhile, and ease our legs.

Thieves [*with an enormous flourish of various sorts of weapons*]. Stand !

Travellers [*in a state of panic*]. Jesu bless us !

100 *Fal.* [*waving his sword*]. Strike ; down with them ; cut the villains' throats : ah ! plaguey caterpillars ! bacon-fed knaves ! they hate us youth : down with them : fleece them.

[*Runs his sword through a traveller's cloak and wrenches it off.*

Travellers. O, we are undone, both we and ours for ever !

Fal. [*belabouring them*]. Hang ye, knaves, are ye un-done ?   No, ye fat chuffs ; I would your store were 110 here !   On, bacons, on !   What, ye knaves ! young men must live.

[*They rob and bind them, and go out, leaving them sighing and groaning by the wayside.   Re-enter* PRINCE HAL *and* POINS, *disguised.*

Prince [*aside*]. The thieves have bound the true men.   Now could thou and I rob the thieves and go merrily to London, it would be argument for a week, laughter for a month, and a good jest for ever.

Poins. Stand close ; I hear them coming.

120   [*Enter the* Thieves *again.*]

Fal. [*in high feather*]. Come, my masters, let us share, and then to horse before day.   And the Prince and Poins be not two arrant cowards, there's no

---

109. *Fat chuffs,* Fat boors.   Bring out the very human joy Falstaff takes in heaping insults as to bulk on some one else.
123. *Arrant,* Downright.

equity stirring : [*disgustedly*] there's no more valour
in that Poins than in a wild duck.

    [*They produce bags of money, and, with watchful
        and furtive gestures, begin to share it. The
        PRINCE and POINS dash out of hiding.*

  Prince. Your money !

130   [*Threatens* FALSTAFF *with drawn sword.*

  Poins. Villains !

    [BARLOLPH, PETO, *and* GADSHILL *tumble over one
        another in their efforts to beat a hasty retreat.
        *FALSTAFF, after a blow or two, runs away too.
        The booty is left, and* POINS *and the* PRINCE
        gather it up.*

  Prince. Got with much ease. Now merrily to horse :

    [*Stepping to side of the stage and looking as if after
        the thieves.*

140 The thieves are all scatter'd and posses'd with fear
So strongly that they dare not meet each other ;
Each takes his fellow for an officer.
Away, good Ned. [*Looks again.*] Falstaff sweats to
    death,
And lards the lean earth as he walks along :
Were't not for laughing, I should pity him.

  Poins. How the rogue roar'd !

            [*They go out together in high delight.*

CURTAIN

SCENE III

As in Scene I. PRINCE HAL *and* POINS *are drinking
at the table.*

[*Enter* FRANCIS.]

  Fran. My lord, old Sir John, with half a dozen more
are at the door : shall I let them in ?

  Prince. Open the door.

[*Enter* Falstaff, Gadshill, Bardolph, *and* Peto.
Francis *brings wine.*]

10 *Poins.* Welcome, Jack : where hast thou been ?

Fal. [*seating himself heavily on the settle*]. A plague of
all cowards, I say, and a vengeance too ! marry, and
amen ! Give me a cup of sack, boy. Ere I lead this
life long, I'll sew nether stocks and mend them and
foot them too. [*Eyeing* Hal *and* Poins *with lofty disdain*] A plague of all cowards ! Give me a cup of
sack, rogue. Is there no virtue extant ?

[*He takes a tankard from* Francis, *and drinks.*

Prince. Didst thou ever see Titan kiss a dish of
20 butter ? pitiful-hearted Titan, that melted at the
sweet tale of the sun's ! if thou didst, then behold that
compound.

Fal. [*to* Francis]. You rogue, here's lime in this
sack too : there is nothing but roguery to be found in
villainous man : yet a coward is worse than a cup of
sack with lime in it. A villainous coward ! [*As if
soliloquizing, shaking his head over his tankard*] Go thy
ways, old Jack ; die when thou wilt, if manhood, good
manhood, be not forgot upon the face of the earth,
30 then am I a shotten herring. There live not three
good men unhanged in England ; and one of them is
fat and grows old : God help the while ! a bad world,
I say. I would I were a weaver, I could sing psalms
or anything. A plague of all cowards, I say still.

Prince [*putting down his wine-cup and coming forward*]. How now, wool-sack ! what mutter you ?

Fal. [*with an expression of unutterable scorn*]. A
king's son ! If I do not beat thee out of thy kingdom

---

23. *Lime,* Put in Spanish sack to preserve it.
30. *Shotten,* Having shed its roe.
33. *Weaver.* Many Calvinistic Flemish weavers, to avoid the
religious persecution instigated by Spain, fled to London.
Their psalm-singing is often alluded to.

with a dagger of lath, and drive all thy subjects afore
40 thee like a flock of wild-geese, I'll never wear hair on
my face more.   You Prince of Wales !

[*He makes a gesture of disgust at the rulings of
Fate.*

Prince. Why, you plaguey round man, what's the
matter ?

Fal. Are you not a coward ? answer me to that :
and Poins there.

Poins [*hand on dagger*]. Zounds, ye fat paunch, an
ye call me coward, by the Lord I'll stab thee.

50 *Fal.* I call thee coward ! No, I'll not call thee
coward, but I would give a thousand pound I could
run as fast as thou canst.   You are straight enough in
the shoulders, you care not who sees your back : call
you that backing of your friends ?   A plague upon
such backing ! give me them that will face me.   Give
me a cup of sack : I am a rogue, if I drunk to-day.

Prince. O villain ! thy lips are scarce wiped since
thou drunkest last.

Fal. [*quite unconcerned*]. All's one for that. [*He
60 drinks.*]   A plague of all cowards, still say I.

Prince. What's the matter ?

Fal. What's the matter ! there be four of us here
have ta'en a hundred pounds this day morning.

Prince. Where is it, Jack ? where is it ?

Fal. [*with a look of measureless indignation*]. Where
is it ! taken from us it is : a hundred upon poor four
of us.

[*Looks from the* PRINCE *to* POINS *to see the effect of
this.*

70 *Prince.* What, a hundred, man ?

Fal. [*with solemn impressiveness*]. I am a rogue, if I

---

39. *Dagger of lath.* Two comic characters, the Vice and the
Devil, appear in the old morality plays, and their tricks provide a good deal of rough fun. The Vice carries a wooden
dagger, and with it belabours the blustering but cowardly
Devil.

were not at half-sword with a dozen of them two hours
together. I have 'scaped by miracle. I am eight
times thrust through the doublet, four through the
hose; my buckler cut through and through; my
sword hacked like a handsaw—*ecce signum!* [*He
draws it.*] I never dealt better since I was a man: all
would not do. A plague of all cowards! [*Regards
the* PRINCE *and* POINS *with the flashing eye of the justly*
80 *indignant.*] Let them speak: if they speak more or
less than truth, they are villains and the sons of darkness.   [*Indicates the three other thieves.*

Prince. Speak, sirs; how was it?

Gads. We four set upon some dozen——

Fal. Sixteen at least, my lord.

Gads. And bound them.

Peto. No, no, they were not bound.

Fal. You rogue, they were bound, every man of
them; or I am a Jew else, an Ebrew Jew.

90 *Gads.* As we were sharing, some six or seven fresh
men set upon us——

Fal. And unbound the rest, and then come in the
other.

Prince. What, fought you with them all?

Fal. All! I know not what you call all; but if I
fought not with fifty of them, I am a bunch of radish:
if there were not two or three and fifty upon poor old
Jack, then am I no two-legged creature.

Prince. Pray God you have not murdered some of
100 them.

Fal. Nay, that's past praying for: I have peppered
two of them; two I am sure I have paid, two rogues in
buckram suits. I tell thee what, Hal, if I tell thee a
lie, spit in my face, call me horse. [*Rises, and with the
careful motion of a fat man, crosses to the centre of the*

---

72. *At half-sword,* Fighting at close quarters, the distance of half
a sword.
76. *Ecce signum,* Behold the sign, see the proof. He has hacked
his sword with his own dagger.

*stage, and, drawing his sword, takes up an attitude of
fence.*] Thou knowest my old ward; here I lay and
thus I bore my point. Four rogues in buckram let
drive at me——

110   *Prince.* What, four? thou saidst but two even
now.

   Fal. Four, Hal; I told thee four.

   Poins [*propitiatingly*]. Ay, ay, he said four.

   Fal. These four came all a-front, and mainly thrust
at me. I made me no more ado, but took all their
seven points in my target, thus.

      [*Whips his buckler from imaginary point to point
        of the swords of the seven and strikes an attitude,
        looking at* HAL.

120   *Prince.* Seven? why, there were but four even now.

   Fal. In buckram?

   Poins. Ay, four, in buckram suits.

   Fal. Seven, by these hilts, or I am a villain else.

   Prince [*aside, to* POINS]. Prithee, let him alone; we
shall have more anon.

   Fal. Dost thou hear me, Hal?

   Prince. Ay, and mark thee too, Jack.

   Fal. Do so, for it is worth the listening to. These
nine in buckram that I told thee of——

130   *Prince.* So, two more already.

   Fal. Their points being broken, began to give me
ground: but I followed me close, came in foot and
hand; and with a thought seven of the eleven I paid.

   Prince [*aside*]. O monstrous! eleven buckram men
grown out of two!

   Fal. But, as the devil would have it, three mis-
begotten knaves in Kendal green came at my back
and let drive at me; for it was so dark, Hal, that
thou couldst not see thy hand.

140   *Prince.* These lies are like their father that begets

---

107. *Ward,* The attitude taken up to protect oneself, but, unlike
    the modern " parry," having something of the offensive as
    well as the defensive.

them ; gross as a mountain, open, palpable. Why, thou knotty-pated fool, thou plaguey, greasy tallow-keech——

Fal. [*rolling an outraged eye*]. What, art thou mad ? art thou mad ? is not the truth the truth ?

Prince. Why, how couldst thou know these men in Kendal green, when it was so dark thou couldst not see thy hand ? come, tell us your reason : what sayest thou to this ?

150 *Poins* [*clapping his shoulder*]. Come, your reason, Jack, your reason.

Fal. What, upon compulsion ? Zounds, an I were at the strappado, or all the racks in the world, I would not tell you on compulsion. Give you a reason on compulsion ! if reasons were as plentiful as blackberries, I would give no man a reason upon compulsion, I.

Prince. I'll be no longer guilty of this sin ; this sanguine coward, this horseback-breaker, this huge
160 hill of flesh——

Fal. [*at once ready with his part in this game of epithets*]. 'Sblood, you starveling, you elf-skin, you dried neat's tongue, you stock-fish ! O for breath to utter what is like thee ! you tailor's-yard, you sheath, you bow-case, you vile standing-tuck——

Prince. Well, breathe awhile, and then to it again : and when thou hast tired thyself in base comparisons, hear me speak this.

Poins. Mark, Jack.

170 *Prince.* We two saw you four set on four and bound them, and were masters of their wealth. Mark now, how a plain tale shall put you down. Then did we

---

142. *Tallow-keech,* Lump of fat.
153. *Strappado,* A military punishment. A man was pulled up by his arms, which were strapped behind his back, and suddenly allowed to fall, so that his arms were broken and his bones put out of joint.
163. *Neat,* An ox or a cow.
163. *Stock-fish,* Dried cod.
165. *Tuck,* Rapier.

two set on you four, and, with a word, out-faced you
from your prize, and have it; yea, and can show it
you here in the house: and Falstaff, you carried yourself away as nimbly, and with as quick dexterity, and
roared for mercy, and still run and roared, as ever I
heard bull-calf. What a slave art thou, to hack thy
sword as thou hast done, and say it was in fight!
180 What a trick, what device, what starting-hole, canst
thou now find out to hide thee from this open and
apparent shame?

Poins. Come, let's hear, Jack; what trick hast thou
now?

Fal. [*whose face has been a study during* HAL'S *re-
cital*]. By the Lord, I knew ye as well as he that made
ye. Why, hear you, my master: was it for me to kill
the heir-apparent [*looking reverently at* HAL] should
I turn upon the true prince? why, thou knowest I
190 am as valiant as Hercules, but beware instinct; the
lion will not touch the true prince. Instinct is a great
matter; I was a coward on instinct. I shall think the
better of myself and thee during my life; I for a
valiant lion, and thou for a true prince. But, by the
Lord, lads, I am glad you have the money. Hostess,
clap to the doors: watch to-night, pray to-morrow.
Gallants, lads, boys, hearts of gold, all the titles of
good fellowship come to you! What, shall we be
merry? Shall we have a song?

200 [FRANCIS *brings wine and goes out: they drink, and
sing, " And let me the canakin clink," or some
other old drinking-song.*

[FRANCIS *re-enters hastily, with an alarmed expression.*]

Francis. O, my lord the prince, there's villainous
news abroad. Percy of the north, and Glendower of
Wales, and his son-in-law Mortimer, and old Northumberland, and that Scot of Scots, Douglas, march

173. *Out-faced*, Frightened. 180. *Starting-hole*, Place of refuge.

against your father. You must to the court in the morning.

210 *Fal.* Tell me, Hal, art not thou horrible afeard ? thou being heir-apparent, could the world pick thee out three such enemies again as that fiend Douglas, that spirit Percy, and that devil Glendower ? Art thou not horribly afraid ? doth not thy blood thrill at it ?

Prince. Not a whit, i' faith ; I lack some of thy instinct.

[*A loud knocking heard.* BARDOLPH *and* FRANCIS *go out.*

220   [*Re-enter* BARDOLPH, *running.*]

Bard. O, my lord, my lord ! the sheriff with a most monstrous watch is at the door !

Fal. Out, ye rogue.

[*Re-enter* FRANCIS.]

Fran. O, my lord, my lord !

Prince. What's the matter ?

Fran. The sheriff and all the watch are at the door : they are come to search the house. Shall I let them in ?

230 *Fal.* Let the sheriff enter : if I become not a cart as well as another man, a plague on my bringing up ! I hope I shall as soon be strangled with a halter as another.

Prince. Go, hide thee behind the arras : the rest walk up above. Now, my masters, for a true face and good conscience. [*Assumes a look of sober dignity.*

Fal. Both which I have had : but their date is out, and therefore I'll hide me. [*Goes behind the arras.*

Prince. Call in the sheriff.

240   [*Exeunt all but the* PRINCE *and* PETO.

230. *Cart, i.e.* That in which a highwayman was conveyed to the gallows.

[*Enter* Sheriff.]

Now, master sheriff, what is your will with me?

Sher. [*bowing*]. First, pardon me, my lord. A hue and cry
Hath follow'd certain men unto this house.

Prince. What men?

Sher. One of them is well known, my gracious lord,
A gross fat man, as fat as butter.

Prince. The man, I do assure you, is not here;
250 For I myself at this time have employed him.
And, sheriff, I will engage my word to thee
That I will, by to-morrow dinner-time,
Send him to answer thee, or any man,
For anything he shall be charged withal:
And so let me entreat you leave the house.

Sher. [*with a doubtful look at the arras*]. I will, my lord. There are two gentlemen
Have in this robbery lost three hundred marks.

Prince. It may be so: if he have robb'd these
260 men,
He shall be answerable; and so farewell.

Sher. Good-night, my noble lord.

Prince. I think it is good-morrow, is it not?

Sher. Indeed, my lord, I think it be two o'clock.

[*Exit* Sheriff.

Prince. This oily rascal is known as well as Paul's.
Go call him forth.

Peto. Falstaff! [*No answer but a loud snore.*] Falstaff! [*He draws aside the arras and displays him fast
270 asleep.*] Fast asleep behind the arras, and snorting like a horse.

Prince. Hark, how hard he fetches breath. Search his pockets. [*He searches his pockets and finds certain papers.*] What hast thou found?

Peto. Nothing but papers, my lord.

Prince. Let's see what they be: read them.

Peto [*reads*].

Item, A capon	2s.	2d.
Item, Sauce		4d.
Item, Sack, two gallons	5s.	8d.
Item, Anchovies and sack after supper	2s.	6d.
Item, Bread		ob.

Prince. O monstrous! but one half-pennyworth of bread to this intolerable deal of sack! What there is else, keep close; we'll read it at more advantage: there let him sleep till day. I'll to the court in the morning. We must all to the wars, and thy place shall be honourable. I'll procure this fat rogue a charge of foot; and I know his death will be a march of twelve-score. The money shall be paid back again with advantage. Be with me betimes in the morning; and so, good-morrow, Peto.

Peto. Good-morrow, good my lord.

[*He stands aside, while the* PRINCE *picks up his sword from the table, buckles it on, and having stuck the tavern bill on the chest of the unconscious* FALSTAFF, *goes out.*

CURTAIN

282. *Ob,* Obolus, a half-penny.
285. *At more advantage,* At a more suitable time.
291. *With advantage,* With interest.

THE ENGLISH TRAITORS

(From *Henry V.*)

PERSONS OF THE PLAY

HENRY V., *King of England.*
DUKE OF GLOUCESTER, *brother to the king.*
EARL OF WESTMORELAND.
DUKE OF EXETER, *uncle to the king.*
LORD SCROOP, *apparently the king's best friend, but traitor to him.*
EARL OF CAMBRIDGE, } *also traitors to the king.*
SIR THOMAS GREY,
A Herald, *who speaks the Prologue.*
Attendants.

Situation.—Henry V. of England is on the point of invading France, the crown of which country he claims through his great-great-grandmother, who was a French princess. Three English traitors have conspired to take his life before he sets sail from Southampton.

Time of event of the play : 1415.
Time occupied in acting the play : 25 minutes.

NOTE ON COSTUME

All the persons in this little play are prepared for war, and all, except the attendants, are armed. It would be impossible to represent the complete chain and plate armour of the period in dressing up for a school play. An effective scheme is to let the various characters wear the surcoat, a sort of tunic, of varying lengths, embroidered with a coat of arms (the use of appliqué is of

93

course preferable to embroidery for stage effect), which was slipped on over the armour to keep it from rusting. Grey knitted " jumpers " often look very like chain mail at a distance, and may be worn under the surcoats, the neck and sleeves showing. Long gauntlet gloves may be covered with silver-grey material to suggest the mailed gauntlet, and hockey or cricketing pads, similarly covered, may be worn as greaves. Helmets may be made from the crowns of close-fitting " pull-on " hats, covered with gold or silver.

The attendants should wear short wide-sleeved tunics, long stockings of contrasting colours, soft flat shoes, and either the " sugar-bag " caps or the peaked hoods to be seen in illustrations of history books or tales about the fifteenth century. They should carry tall spears or banners, easily made by the artists of the class from stiff paper painted with a coat of arms against an effective background, and mounted on long silvered poles.

[*Flourish of trumpets, or a few bars of stirring martial music on the piano. Enter* Herald, *to speak the Prologue.*]

PROLOGUE

Now all the youth of England are on fire,
And silken dalliance in the wardrobe lies :
Now thrive the armourers, and honour's thought
Reigns solely in the breast of every man :
They sell the pasture now to buy the horse,
Following the mirror of all Christian kings,
With winged heels, as English Mercuries.
The French, advised by good intelligence
10 Of this most dreadful preparation,
Shake in their fear and with pale policy
Seek to divert the English purposes,
O England ! model to thy inward greatness,

---

3. *Silken dalliance.* Both gay trifling (dalliance) and the gay
      clothes associated with it are laid away.
11. *Policy,* Cunning.

Like little body with a mighty heart,
What mightest thou do, that honour would thee do,
Were all thy children kind and natural !
But see thy fault ! France hath in thee found out
A nest of hollow bosoms, which he fills
With treacherous crowns ; and three corrupted men,
20 One, Richard Earl of Cambridge, and the second,
Henry, Lord Scroop of Masham, and the third,
Sir Thomas Grey, knight, of Northumberland,
Have, for the gilt of France—O guilt indeed !
Confirmed conspiracy with fearful France ;
And by their hands this grace of kings must die,
If hell and treason hold their promises.

*[He draws aside the curtains or takes down the
    screens to show the scene.*

SCENE I

*A council-chamber at Southampton. To the left is a
chair of state, covered with a crimson cloth ; to the right
a table, at which sit* EXETER, BEDFORD, *and* WEST-
MORELAND, *occupied with various papers.*

Bed. [*gravely*]. 'Fore God, his grace is bold, to trust
    these traitors.
Exe. They shall be apprehended by-and-by.
West. [*with a sort of wondering disgust*]. How smooth
10   and even they do bear themselves !
As if allegiance in their bosoms sat,
Crownèd with faith and constant loyalty.
Bed. The king hath note of all that they intend,
By interception which they dream not of.
Exe. [*as if he can hardly believe it*]. Nay, but the
    man that was his bedfellow,

---

14. *Interception,* An interruption of their communications.

Whom he hath dull'd and cloy'd with gracious
    favours,
That he should, for a foreign purse, so sell
20 His sovereign's life to death and treachery.

[*Trumpets.* *Enter* KING HENRY, SCROOP, CAM-
    BRIDGE, GREY, *and* Attendants. *The nobles rise
    and bow to the king, who occupies the chair of state.
    *SCROOP *stands at his right hand.*]

    King. Now sits the wind fair, and we will aboard.
My lord of Cambridge, and my kind lord of Masham,
And you, my gentle knight, give me your thoughts :
Think you not that the powers we bear with us
Will cut their passage through the force of France ?
30   *Scroop.* No doubt, my liege, if each man do his best.
    King. I doubt not that ; since we are well per-
    suaded
We carry not a heart with us from hence
That grows not in a fair consent with ours,
Nor leave not one behind that doth not wish
Success and conquest to attend on us.
    Cam. Never was monarch better fear'd and loved
Than is your majesty : there's not, I think, a subject
That sits in heart-grief and uneasiness
40 Under the sweet shade of your government.
    Grey. True : those that were your father's enemies
Have steep'd their galls in honey and do serve you
With hearts create of duty and of zeal.
    King. We therefore have great cause of thankful-
    ness ;
And shall forget the office of our hand,
Sooner than quittance of desert and merit
According to the weight and worthiness.
    Scroop. So service shall with steeled sinews toil,
50 And labour shall refresh itself with hope

21. *Trumpets.* A bugle call, or a few bars of martial music on the
    piano.   28. *Powers,* Armies.
         47. *Quittance,* Requital, reward.

To do your grace incessant services.
    King [*gravely*]. We judge no less. [*With a change of tone*] Uncle of Exeter,
Enlarge the man committed yesterday,
That rail'd against our person : we consider
It was excess of wine that set him on ;
And on his more advice we pardon him.
    [EXETER *searches for a paper, glances over it, and makes a note on it.*
60   *Scroop* [*with virtuous indignation*]. That's mercy, but too much security :
Let him be punish'd, sovereign, lest example
Breed, by his sufferance, more of such a kind.
    King [*looking at him*]. O, let us yet be merciful.
    Cam. [*reasonably*]. So may your highness, and yet punish too.
    Grey [*positively*]. Sir,
You show great mercy, if you give him life,
After the taste of much correction.
70   *King* [*with veiled irony*]. Alas, your too much love and a care of me
Are heavy orisons 'gainst this poor wretch !
If little faults proceeding on distemper
Shall not be wink'd at, how shall we stretch our eye
When capital crimes, chew'd, swallow'd, and digested,
Appear before us ? We'll yet enlarge that man,
Though Cambridge, Scroop, and Grey, in their dear care
And tender preservation of our person
80 Would have him punish'd. And now to our French causes :
Who are the late commissioners ?
    [EXETER *brings sealed parchments from the table, and gives them to the* KING.
    Cam. I one, my lord :
Your highness bade me ask for it to-day.

---

54. *Enlarge*, Set free.   72. *Orisons*, Prayers.

Scroop. So did you me, my liege.

Grey. And I, my royal sovereign.

King [*giving them the parchments*]. Then, Richard
90   Earl of Cambridge, there is yours ;
There yours, Lord Scroop of Masham ; and, sir knight,
Grey of Northumberland, this same is yours :
Read them ; and know, I know your worthiness.

> [*The traitors break the seals, and read their arrests
> on the charge of high treason. Their com-
> placency is banished by fear, shame, and de-
> spair.*

My Lord of Westmoreland, and uncle Exeter,
We will aboard to-night. Why, how now, gentlemen !
100 What see you in these papers that you lose
So much complexion ? Look ye, how they change !
Their cheeks are paper. Why, what read you there
That hath so cowarded and chased your blood
Out of appearance ?

Cam. [*flinging himself on his knees*]. I do confess my
    fault ;
And do submit me to your highness' mercy.

Grey. ⎫
Scroop. ⎬ To which we all appeal.

> [GREY *speaks this appeal clearly :* SCROOP *in a low*
> 110   *voice.* GREY *kneels on one knee, in supplica-*
> *tion for pardon ;* SCROOP *stands with bent head*
> *and folded arms.*

King [*gravely, as one passing sentence, but with a
touch of the anger and bitterness of a man
deeply wronged by other men, though he keeps
these emotions under control*]. The mercy that
    was quick in us but late,
By your own counsel is suppress'd and kill'd :
You must not dare, for shame, to talk of mercy :
120 For your own reasons turn into your bosoms,
As dogs upon their masters, worrying you.

---

117. *Quick,* alive.

See you, my princes and my noble peers,
These English monsters ! My lord of Cambridge here,
You know how apt our love was to accord
To furnish him with all appertinents
Belonging to his honour ; and this man
Hath, for a few light crowns, lightly conspired
To kill us here in Hampton : to the which
This knight, no less for bounty bound to us

130 Than Cambridge is, hath likewise sworn. But, O,
What shall I say to thee, Lord Scroop ? thou cruel,
Ingrateful, savage, and inhuman creature !
Thou that didst bear the key of all my counsels,
That knew'st the very bottom of my soul,
That almost mightst have coined me into gold,
Wouldst thou have practised on me for thy use !
May it be possible, that foreign hire
Could out of thee extract one spark of evil
That might annoy my finger ? 'tis so strange,

140 That, though the truth of it stands off as gross
As black and white, my eye will scarcely see it.
If that same demon that hath gull'd thee thus
Should with his lion gait walk the whole world,
He might return to vasty Tartar back,
And tell the legions " I can never win
A soul so easy as that Englishman's."
O, how hast thou with jealousy infected
The sweetness of affiance ! Show men dutiful ?
Why, so didst thou : seem they grave and learned ?

150 Why, so didst thou : came they of noble family ?
Why, so didst thou : seem they religious ?
Why, so didst thou: [*turning aside*] I will weep for thee :
For this revolt of thine, methinks, is like
Another fall of man. [*Stretching out his arm in com-
    mand to* EXETER] Their faults are open :
Arrest them to the answer of the law ;
And God acquit them of their practices.

147. *Jealousy,* Suspicion.   **157.** *Practices,* Plots.

[CAMBRIDGE *and* GREY *make signs of despair and entreaty ;* SCROOP *stands quite still.*

160 *Exe.* I arrest thee of high treason, by the name of Richard Earl of Cambridge.

[CAMBRIDGE *takes off his sword, and gives it to EXETER, who breaks it and gives it to an Attendant.*

I arrest thee of high treason, by the name of Thomas Grey, knight, of Northumberland.

[GREY *yields his sword in the same way.*

I arrest thee of high treason, by the name of Henry Lord Scroop of Masham.

170 [SCROOP *breaks his own sword across his knee, and flings away the broken pieces.*

Scroop. Our purposes God justly hath discovered ;
And I repent my fault more than my death ;
Which I beseech your highness to forgive,
Although my body pay the price of it.
   Cam. [*striving to justify himself*]. For me, the gold
      of France did not seduce ;
Although I did admit it as a motive
The sooner to effect what I intended :
180 But God be thanked for prevention ;
Which I in sufferance heartily will rejoice,
Beseeching God and you to pardon me.
   Grey. Never did faithful subject more rejoice
At the discovery of most dangerous treason
Than I do at this hour joy o'er myself,
Prevented from a cursèd enterprise :
My fault, but not my body, pardon, sovereign.
   King [*solemnly*]. God quit you in His mercy !   Hear
      your sentence.
190 You have conspir'd against our royal person,
   Join'd with an enemy proclaim'd, and from his coffers
   Receiv'd the golden earnest of our death ;

188. *Quit*, Acquit.
192. *Earnest*, Money paid beforehand as a pledge.

Wherein you would have sold your king to slaughter,
His princes and his peers to servitude,
His subjects to oppression and contempt,
And his whole kingdom into desolation.
Touching our person seek we no revenge ;
But we our kingdom's safety must so tender,
Whose ruin you have sought, that to her laws
200 We do deliver you.   Get you therefore hence,
Poor miserable wretches, to your death :
The taste whereof, God of His mercy give
You patience to endure and true repentance
Of all your dear offences.   Bear them hence.
        [*The traitors are led away, guarded.*
Now forth, dear countrymen : let us deliver
Our puissance into the hand of God,
Putting it straight in expedition.
Cheerly to sea ; the signs of war advance :
210 No king of England, if not king of France !

WAR MARCH

CURTAIN

204. *Dear*, Grievous.   207. *Puissance*, Power.

THE SOLDIER AND THE KING

(From *Henry V.*)

PERSONS OF THE PLAY

HENRY V., *King of England.*
DUKE OF BEDFORD, ⎫
DUKE OF GLOUCESTER, ⎬ *his brothers.*
SIR THOMAS ERPINGHAM, *an old knight.*
GOWER, *an English captain.*
FLUELLEN, *a Welsh captain.*
BATES, ⎫
COURT, ⎬ *soldiers in the English army.*
WILLIAMS, ⎭
MONTJOY, *a French herald.*
An English Herald, *who also speaks the Prologue.*
An Attendant.

Situation.—Henry V. of England is carrying on a campaign in France to make good his claim to the French crown, to which he believes he has a right through his great-great-grandmother Isabella, who was a French princess. Worn out by sickness and famine, the English troops are about to meet the French on the battlefield. The odds are heavily against them, but the spirit of the king is indomitable.

Time of the events of the play : 1415.
Time occupied in acting the play : one hour.

NOTE ON COSTUME

Henry, Bedford, and Gloucester appear as in the former play, and Erpingham's dress is similar to theirs.

The two heralds wear tabards, or short sleeveless coats blazoned respectively with the lions of England and the lilies of France, long stockings of some bright colour, and flat shoes fitting to the shape of the foot and turned over above the ankle. They carry long trumpets. The attendant in Scene I. may be dispensed with, but, wearing a short wide-sleeved tunic, with long stockings of contrasting colours, and carrying a tall spear, he is a decorative figure in the stage picture. Captains and soldiers wear tunics of leather (an old motor-coat may be employed to excellent advantage), or some dark strong material, reaching nearly to the knee, belts with pouches and peaked hoods, or high " sugar-bag " caps turned over to one side. Fluellen wears the flat Monmouth cap of which he speaks on page 114, and for the sake of variety, Gower may have a small round helmet. They are armed with short daggers, pikes (lances), and bills (weapons resembling long-handled battle-axes). Long poles, cardboard, and silver paper or paint may be used in the contriving of these weapons, illustrations to which may easily be found.

PROLOGUE

[Solemn martial music. Enter the English Herald, to speak the Prologue.]*

Now entertain conjecture of a time
When creeping murmur and the poring dark
Fills the wide vessel of the universe.
Proud of their numbers and secure of soul
The confident and over-lusty French
Do the low-rated English play at dice ;
10 And chide the cripple tardy-gaited night,
Who, like a foul and ugly witch, doth limp
So tediously away. The poor condemned English,

---

* The " cutting " of the Prologue to Act IV. for the shortened play has necessitated the changing of two words—" that," in l. 22, to " for," and " yet," in l. 29, to " now."

Like sacrifices, by their watchful fires
Sit patiently and inly ruminate
The morning's danger, and their gesture sad
Investing lank-lean cheeks and war-worn coats
Presenteth them unto the gazing moon
So many horrid ghosts.   O now, who will behold
The royal captain of this ruined band
20 Walking from watch to watch, from tent to tent,
Let him cry " Praise and glory on his head ! "
For every wretch, pining and pale before,
Beholding him, plucks comfort from his looks :
A largess universal like the sun
His liberal eye doth give to every one,
Thawing cold fear, that mean and gentle all
Behold, as may unworthiness define,
A little touch of Harry in the night.
Now sit and see
30 Minding true things by what their mockeries be.
             [*He makes a low bow and goes out.*

SCENE I

*The English camp at Agincourt.   To the left of the
stage, on what appears to be a mound or big stone, sits the
KING, glancing over a communication from which hangs
a great seal.   An* Attendant *stands by him.   Enter
BEDFORD and GLOUCESTER, and salute the KING,
bowing low to him.   He rises and greets them.*

King [*gravely, but with spirit*].   Gloucester, 'tis true
        that we are in great danger ;
10 The greater therefore should our courage be.
   Good-morrow, brother Bedford.   God Almighty !
There is some soul of goodness in things evil,

24. **Largess,** Royal bounty.

Would men observingly distil it out.
For our bad neighbour makes us early stirrers,
Which is both healthful and good husbandry.

[*Enter* SIR THOMAS ERPINGHAM, *and bows to
the* KING.]

Good-morrow, old Sir Thomas Erpingham :
A good soft pillow for that good white head
20 Were better than a churlish turf of France.
 Erp. [*proudly*]. Not so, my liege : this lodging likes
  me better,
Since I may say, " Now lie I like a king."
 King [*laughing*]. Lend me thy cloak, Sir Thomas.
       [SIR THOMAS *gives it to him.*
           Brothers both,
Commend me to the princes in our camp ;
Do my good-morrow to them, and anon
Desire them all to my pavilion.
30 *Glou.* We shall, my liege.
 Erp. Shall I attend your grace ?
 King.   No, my good knight ;
Go with my brothers to my lords of England :
I and my bosom must debate awhile,
And then I would no other company.
  [GLOUCESTER *and* BEDFORD *bow and go out,
   followed by the* Attendant, *to whom* HENRY
   gives the communication he was reading at the
   opening of the scene.* SIR THOMAS ERPING-
40   HAM *kneels on one knee and kisses* HENRY'S
   hand.*
 Erp. The Lord in heaven bless thee, noble Harry !
  [*He goes out.* *The* KING *looks after him.*
 King. God-a-mercy, old heart ! thou speakest
  cheerfully.
  [*He wraps* ERPINGHAM'S *cloak about him, and for*

15. *Good husbandry,* Managing one's life well.
27. *Commend me to,* A courteous message of greeting.

*a moment stands in thought, showing signs of
an anxiety which was not apparent while he was
with other men.*

50 [*Enter* FLUELLEN, *bustling across the stage as if on an
errand of vast importance.* HENRY *stands aside
watching. Enter* GOWER, *hastily.*]

Gower [*loudly*]. Captain Fluellen !

Fluellen [*turning in great consternation, finger on lip,
speaking in what appears to be a lowered voice, with a
strong Welsh accent*]. So ! in the name of Jesu Christ,
speak lower. It is the greatest admiration in the
universal world, when the true and aunchient laws
of the wars is not kept ; if you would take the pains
60 but to examine the wars of Pompey the Great, you
shall find, I warrant you, that there is no tiddle taddle
nor pibble pabble in Pompey's camp ; I warrant you,
you shall find the ceremonies of the wars, and the cares
of it, and the forms of it, and the sobriety of it, and the
modesty of it, to be otherwise.

Gower [*expostulating*]. Why, the enemy is loud :
you hear him all night.

Flu. If the enemy is an ass and a fool and a prating
coxcomb, is it meet, think you, that we should also,
70 look you, be an ass and a fool and a prating coxcomb ?
in your own conscience, now ?

Gower [*quite convinced*]. I will speak lower.

Flu. I pray and beseech you that you will.

[*They go out together,* GOWER *making some sort
of communication to* FLUELLEN, *with gestures
implying great discretion and secrecy, hand up
to his mouth.*

King [*with amused approval*]. Though it appear a
little out of fashion,
80 There is much care and valour in this Welshman.

---

57. *Admiration*, Marvel, wonder.

[*Enter three English soldiers,* JOHN BATES, ALEXANDER
COURT, *and* MICHAEL WILLIAMS. *All are shivering and disconsolate.* BATES *is particularly de-
pressed in appearance.* WILLIAMS, *while thoroughly
miserable, is inclined to be talkative. They lay
down their bills, sit on the ground, bring out hunks
of bread and cheese and a tankard of beer, and begin
to consume a morning meal.*]

Court [*pointing with his dagger, on which is impaled
90 a bit of cheese*]. Brother John Bates, is not that the
morning which breaks yonder ?

Bates [*removing the tankard from his lips to look*]. I
think it be : but we have no great cause to desire the
approach of day.

> [*Takes a pull at the tankard, passes it to* COURT *at
an indignant sign from the latter, and gives a
heavy sigh.*

Will. We see yonder the beginning of the day, but I
think we shall never see the end of it. [*Sees* HENRY,
100 *and springs up, bill in hand.*] Who goes there ?

King. A friend.

Will. Under what captain serve you ?

King. Under Sir Thomas Erpingham.

Will. [*in the tone of a man inclined for a talk*]. A good
old commander and a most kind gentleman : I pray
you, what thinks he of our estate ?

King [*gravely*]. Even as men wrecked upon a sand,
that look to be washed off the next tide.

> [*General consternation.*

110 *Bates.* He hath not told his thought to the king ?

King. No ; nor it is not meet he should. For,
though I speak it to you, I think the king is but a man,
as I am : the violet smells to him as it doth to me ;
the element shows to him as it doth to me : his ceremonies laid by, in his nakedness he appears but a man.
Therefore when he sees reason of fears, as we do, his
fears, out of doubt, be of the same relish as ours are :

yet, in reason, no man should possess him with any appearance of fear, lest he, by showing it, should dis-120 hearten his army.

Bates [sardonically]. He may show what outward courage he will ; but I believe, as cold a night as 'tis, he could wish himself in Thames up to the neck ; and so I would he were, and I by him, at all adventures, so we were quit here.

King [with spirit]. By my troth, I will speak my conscience of the king : I think he would not wish himself anywhere but where he is.

Bates [sighing]. Then I would he were here alone ; 130 so should he be sure to be ransomed, and a many poor men's lives saved.

> [*The others make signs of assent. For a moment* HENRY *seems taken aback, then he recovers himself.*

King [persuasively]. I daresay you love him not so ill, to wish him here alone, howsoever you speak this to feel other men's minds : methinks I could not die any-where so contented as in the king's company ; his cause being just and his quarrel honourable.

140   *Will.* That's more than we know.

Bates [with resignation]. Ay, or more than we should seek after ; for we know enough, if we know we are the king's subjects : if his cause be wrong, our obedi-ence to the king wipes the crime of it out of us.

Will [argumentatively]. But if the cause be not good, the king himself hath a heavy reckoning to make, when all those legs and arms and heads, chopped off in a battle, shall join together at the latter day and cry all, " We died at such a place," some swearing, 150 some crying for a surgeon, some upon their wives left poor behind them, some upon the debts they owe, some upon their children rawly left. I am afeard there are few die well that die in a battle ; for how can they charitably dispose of anything, when blood is their argument ? Now, if these men do not die

well, it will be a black matter for the king that led
them to it ; whom to disobey were against all proportion of subjection.

[*The others make sounds of agreement.*

160 *King.* So, if a son that is by his father sent about
merchandise do sinfully miscarry upon the sea, the
imputation of his wickedness, by your rule, should be
imposed upon his father that sent him ; or if a servant,
under his master's command transporting a sum of
money, be assailed by robbers and die in many irre-
conciled iniquities, you may call the business of the
master the author of the servant's damnation : but
this is not so ; the king is not bound to answer the
particular endings of his soldiers, the father of his son,
170 nor the master of his servant ; for they purpose not
their death, when they purpose their services. . . . If
men have defeated the law and outrun native punishment, though they can outstrip men, they have no
wings to fly from God : war is His beadle, war is His
vengeance. Every subject's duty is the king's ; but
every subject's soul is his own.

Will. [*impressed*]. 'Tis certain, every man that dies
ill, the ill upon his own head, the king is not to
answer it.

180 *Bates* [*gloomily, but with British bull-dog determina-
tion*]. I do not desire he should answer for me : and
yet I determine to fight lustily for him.

King [*encouraged by the effect of his words*]. I
myself heard the king say he would not be ransomed.

Will. [*with the air of a man not to be taken in by
that sort of thing*]. Ay, he said so, to make us fight
cheerfully : but when our throats are cut, he may
be ransomed, and we ne'er the wiser.

161. *Miscarry,* Come to harm.
165. *Die in many iniquities, i.e.* Without having the opportunity to
   confess his sins and receive absolution.
172. *Native,* In their own country.

190 *King* [*angrily*]. If I live to see it, I will never trust his word after.

Will. [*mocking him*]. You pay him, then. [*Sarcastically*] That's a perilous shot out of an elder-gun, that a poor and a private displeasure can do against a monarch! you may as well go about to turn the sun to ice by fanning in his face with a peacock's feather. *You'll* never trust his word after! come, 'tis a foolish saying.

King. Your reproof is something too round: I 200 should be angry with you, if the time were convenient.

Will. [*ready for anything*]. Let it be a quarrel between us, if you live.

King [*grimly*]. I embrace it.

Will. How shall I know thee again?

King. Give me any gage of thine, and I will wear it in my bonnet: then, if ever thou darest acknowledge it, I will make it my quarrel.

Will. Here's my glove [*gives him a gauntlet*]: give me another of thine.

210 *King* [*giving it*]. There.

Will. This will I also wear in my cap: if ever thou come to me and say, after to-morrow, "This is my glove," by this hand, I will take thee a box on the ear.

King. If ever I live to see it, I will challenge it.

Will. Thou darest as well be hanged.

King. Well, I will do it, though I take thee in the king's company.

Will. Keep thy word: fare thee well.

[*They bow to one another with mock ceremony.*

220 *Bates* [*growling*]. Be friends, you English fools, be friends: we have French quarrels enow, if you could tell how to reckon.

King. Indeed, the French may lay twenty French crowns to one, they will beat us; for they bear them

---

193. *Elder-gun*, Pop-gun.   199. *Round*, Direct.
205. *Gage*, Pledge.   206. *Bonnet*, Cap.
                    221. *Enow*, Enough.

on their shoulders : but it is no English treason to
cut French crowns, and to-morrow the king himself
will be a clipper.

> [*A trumpet sounds without. In a somewhat*
> *leisurely way, the soldiers gather together their*
> 230 *belongings and go out. Left to himself, the*
> KING *stands with folded arms for a minute,*
> *as if in reverie. He has always believed that*
> *his men would willingly follow him to the death,*
> *and though he knows enough of human nature*
> *to understand their present attitude, he feels a*
> *passing bitterness, and a sudden mistrust in*
> *himself and his ultimate success.*

> [*Enter* ERPINGHAM.]

Erp. My lord, your nobles, jealous of your absence,
240 Seek through your camp to find you.
    King.   Good old knight,
Collect them all together at my tent :
I'll be before thee.

> [*He takes off* ERPINGHAM'S *cloak and gives it back*
> *to him. The old knight looks at him as if he*
> *noticed some change of mood in him.*
    Erp.   I shall do't, my lord.

> [*He goes out.*
> [*Holding his sword before him, hands clasped over*
> 250 *its cross hilt,* HENRY *kneels and prays.*
    King. O God of battles ! steel my soldiers' hearts ;
Possess them not with fear ; take from them now
The sense of reckoning, if the opposed numbers
Pluck their hearts from them. Not to-day, O Lord,
O not to-day, think not upon the fault
My father made in compassing the crown !

---

227. *Clipper*, One who "clipped" parings of silver or gold from
    coins—a common offence before coins were made with
    milled edges.
239. *Jealous of*, Suspicious of, anxious about.
256. *My father.* Henry's father, Henry Bolingbroke, had usurped
    the crown from the weak and unjust Richard II.

I Richard's body have interred new ;
And on it have bestowed more contrite tears
Than from it issued forced drops of blood :
260 Five hundred poor I have in yearly pay,
Who twice a day their withered hands hold up
Toward heaven, to pardon blood ; and I have built
Two chantries, where the sad and solemn priests
Sing still for Richard's soul.   More will I do ;
Though all that I can do is nothing worth,
Since that my penitence comes after all,
Imploring pardon.

[*Enter* GLOUCESTER.]

   Glou.   My liege !
270   *King.* My brother Gloucester's voice ? Ay ;
I know thy errand, I will go with thee :
The day, my friends, and all things stay for me.
               [*They go out.   Martial music.*

CURTAIN

SCENE II

*The field of Agincourt.   Without, a confused noise of
battle, cries, swords clashing on shields, bugle calls, etc.*

[*Enter the* KING, BEDFORD, GLOUCESTER, FLUELLEN,
a Herald, BATES, COURT, *and* WILLIAMS.]

   King. I was not angry since I came to France
Until this instant.   Take a trumpet, herald ;
Ride thou unto the horsemen on yon hill :
If they will fight with us, bid them come down,
10 Or void the field ; they do offend our sight :
If they'll do neither, we will come to them.
And make them skirr away, as swift as stones

12. *Skirr,* Rush swiftly.

Enforced from the old Assyrian slings :
Besides, we'll cut the throats of those we have
And not a man of them that we shall take
Shall taste our mercy.   Go and tell them so.

[*Exit* Herald.

[*Enter* Montjoy.]

Bed. Here comes the herald of the French, my
20   liege.
Glou. His eyes are humbler than they used to be.
King. How now ! what means this, herald ?
Mont.   Oh, great king,
I come to thee for charitable license,
That we may wander o'er this bloody field,
To look our dead, and then to bury them.
King.   I tell thee truly, herald,
I know not if the day be ours or no ;
For yet a many of your horsemen peer
30 And gallop o'er the field.
Mont.   The day is yours.
King. Praised be God, and not our strength,
for it !
What is this castle called that stands hard by ?
Mont. They call it Agincourt.
King. Then call we this the field of Agincourt,
Fought on the day of Crispin Crispianus.
Flu. [*unable to contain his pride and excitement any
longer*]. Your grandfather of famous memory, an't
40 please your majesty, and your great-uncle Edward
the Plack Prince of Wales, as I have read in the
chronicles, fought a most prave pattle here in
France.
King. They did, Fluellen.
Flu. Your majesty says very true : if your majesty
is remembered of it, the Welshmen did good service
in a garden where leeks did grow, wearing leeks in

24. *License*, Permission.

their Monmouth caps ; which, your majesty knows, to this hour is an honourable badge of the service ;
50 and I do believe your majesty takes no scorn to wear the leek upon Saint Tavy's day.

King. I wear it for a memorable honour ;
For I am Welsh, you know, good countryman.

Flu. All the water in Wye cannot wash your majesty's Welsh plood out of your pody, I can tell you that : God pless it and preserve it, as long as it pleases his grace, and his majesty too !

King. Thanks, good my countryman.

Flu. [*seizing the* KING *by the hand*]. By Jeshu, I am
60 your majesty's countryman, I care not who know it ; I will confess it to all the 'orld : I need not be ashamed of your majesty, praised be God, so long as your majesty is an honest man.

King. God keep me so ! [*To* MONTJOY] Go with your heralds,
Bring me just notice of the numbers dead
On both our parts. [*To* FLUELLEN] Call yonder fellow hither.   [*Points to* WILLIAMS.
                                        [*Exit* MONTJOY.

70 *Flu.* [*with much pomp*]. Soldier, you must come to the king.

        [WILLIAMS *comes forward, and does obeisance to
        the* KING, *kneeling on one knee.*

King. Soldier, why wearest thou that glove in thy cap ?

Will. An't please your majesty, 'tis the gage of one that I should fight withal, if he be alive.

King. An Englishman ?

Will. An't please your majesty, a rascal that
80 swaggered with me last night ; who, if alive and ever dared to challenge this glove, I have sworn to take him a box o' th' ear : or if I can see my glove in his cap, which he swore, as he was a soldier, he would wear if alive, I will strike it out soundly.

King [*solemnly to* FLUELLEN]. What think you,

Captain Fluellen? is it fit this soldier keep his oath?

Flu. [*with emphasis*]. He is a craven and a villain else, an't please your majesty, in my conscience.

90 *King.* It may be his enemy is a gentleman of great sort.

Flu. Though he be as good a gentleman as the devil is, as Lucifer and Beelzebub himself, it is necessary, look your grace, that he keep his vow and his oath: if he be perjured, see you now, his reputation is as arrant a villain and a Jacksauce, as ever his plack shoe trod upon God's ground and his earth, in my conscience, la!

King. Then keep thy vow, sirrah, when thou
100 meetest the fellow.

Will. So I will, my liege, as I live.

King. Who servest thou under?

Will. Under Captain Gower, my liege.

Flu. [*approvingly*]. Gower is a good captain, and is good knowledge and literatured in the wars.

King. Call him hither to me, soldier.

Will. I will, my liege.

[*He goes out.* HENRY *takes* FLUELLEN *aside, as if to confer with him on some matter of great*
110 *importance.*

King [*giving* FLUELLEN WILLIAMS'S *glove*]. Here, Fluellen; wear thou this favour for me and stick it in thy cap: when Alençon and myself were down together, I plucked this glove from his helm: if any man challenge this, he is a friend to Alençon and an enemy to our person; if thou encounter any such, apprehend him, an thou dost me love.

Flu. [*almost beside himself*]. Your grace doo's me as great honours as can be desired in the hearts of his
120 subjects: I would fain see the man, that has but two legs, that shall find himself aggriefed at this

---

91. *Sort,* Rank.   96. *Arrant,* Thorough.

glove ; that is all ; but I would fain see it once, an please God of his grace that I might see.

[*Fixes the glove in his cap and goes out with a distinct swagger.*

CURTAIN

SCENE III

Another part of the field of Agincourt.

[*Enter* GOWER *and* WILLIAMS, GOWER *in a state of pleased apprehension.*]

Will. I warrant it is to knight you, captain.

[*Enter* FLUELLEN.]

Flu. [*bustling up to* GOWER]. God's will and his pleasure, captain, I beseech you now, come apace to the king : there is more good toward you peradven-
10 ture than is in your knowledge to dream of.

Will. [*in mighty wrath, plucking the glove from his cap and thrusting it before* FLUELLEN]. Sir, know you this glove ?

Flu. [*amazed*]. Know the glove ! I know the glove is a glove.

Will. [*flicking the glove* FLUELLEN *wears in his cap*]. I know this ; and thus I challenge it.   [*Strikes him.*

Flu. 'Sblood ! an arrant traitor as any is in the universal world, or in France, or in England !

20 *Gow.* [*seizing* WILLIAMS]. How now, sir ! you villain !

Will. [*struggling*]. Do you think I'll be forsworn ?

Flu. Stand away, Captain Gower ; I will give treason his payment into plows, I warrant you.

Will. [*furiously*]. I am no traitor.

Flu. That's a lie in thy throat. I charge you in his

majesty's name, apprehend him : he's a friend of the
Duke Alençon's.

[*Enter* GLOUCESTER.]

30 *Glou.* How now, how now ! what's the matter ?

Flu. My lord, here is—praised be God for it !—a
most contagious treason come to light, look you, as
you shall desire in a summer's day.   Here is his
majesty.

[*Enter* KING HENRY *and* BEDFORD.]

King. How now ! what's the matter ?

Flu. My liege, here is a villain and a traitor, that,
look your grace, has struck the glove which your
majesty is take out of the helmet of Alençon.

40 *Will.* My liege, this was my glove ; here is the
fellow of it ; and he that I gave it to in change promised to wear it in his cap : I promised to strike him
if he did : I met this man with my glove in his cap,
and I have been as good as my word.

Flu. [*with growing excitement*]. Your majesty hear
now, saving your majesty's manhood, what an arrant,
rascally, beggarly knave it is : I hope your majesty
will pear me testimony and witness, and will avouch-
ment, that this is the glove of Alençon, that your
50 majesty is give me ; in your conscience, now.

[*Glares at* WILLIAMS.

King. Give me thy glove, soldier [WILLIAMS *does so*] :
look, here is the fellow of it. [WILLIAMS *stares in
horror as the truth dawns on him.*]
'Twas I, indeed, thou promised'st to strike ;
And thou hast given me most bitter terms.

Flu. And please your majesty, let his neck answer
for it, if there is any martial law in the 'orld.

King [*gravely*]. How canst thou make me satisfac-
60 tion ?

Will. [*manfully*]. All offences, my lord, come from

the heart : never came any from mine that might offend your majesty.

King. It was ourself thou didst abuse.

Will. Your majesty came not like yourself : you appeared to me but as a common man ; witness the night, your garments, your lowliness ; and what your highness suffered under that shape, I beseech you take it for your own fault, and not mine : for had you been 70 as I took you for, I made no offence ; therefore, I beseech your highness, pardon me.

King. Here, brother Gloucester, fill this glove with crowns,
And give it to this fellow. Keep it, fellow,
And wear it for an honour in thy cap
Till I do challenge it. Give him the crowns.

[GLOUCESTER *does so.*

And, captain, you must needs be friends with him.

Flu. [*patronizingly*]. By this day and this light, the 80 fellow has mettle enough. [*With an air*] Hold, there is twelve pence for you ; and I pray you to serve God, and keep you out of prawls, and prabbles, and quarrels, and dissensions, and, I warrant you, it is the petter for you.

Will. [*with dignity*]. I will none of your money.

Flu. It is with a good will ; I can tell you, it will serve to mend your shoes : come, wherefore should you be so pashful ? your shoes is not so good : 'tis a good shilling, I warrant you, or I will change it.

90   [*Urges the shilling on the reluctant* WILLIAMS, *who is at last obliged to take it.*

[*Enter the* English Herald.]

King. Now, herald, are the dead numbered ?

Her. [*giving him a paper*]. Here is the number of the slaughtered French.

King. This note doth tell me of ten thousand French
That in the field lie slain.

Where is the number of our English dead ?

                         [Herald *shows him another paper.*

100 But nine and twenty ! O God, thy arm was here ;
And not to us, but to thy arm alone,
Ascribe we all.   Do we all holy rites ;
Let there be sung " Non nobis " and " Te Deum " ;
The dead with charity enclosed in clay :
And then to Calais ; and to England then,
Where ne'er from France arrived more happy men.

                         [*Solemn music.   They pass out.*

CURTAIN

THE POUND OF FLESH

(From *The Merchant of Venice*)

PERSONS OF THE PLAY

SHYLOCK, *a rich Jewish money-lender*
ANTONIO, *a merchant of Venice.*
BASSANIO, *chief friend to Antonio.*
GRATIANO,
SALARINO, } *young Venetian gentlemen, friends to Antonio*
SALANIO, *and Bassanio.*
LORENZO,
The DUKE OF VENICE.
TUBAL, *a Jew, friend to Shylock.*
LAUNCELOT GOBBO, *servant to Shylock.*
PORTIA, *a rich heiress, whom Bassanio weds.*
NERISSA, *her lady-in-waiting, whom Gratiano weds.*
JESSICA, *the daughter of Shylock.*
Attendants, Masquers, a Clerk.

    Time of the story of the play : sixteenth century.
    Time occupied in acting the play : one hour and a
    half.

NOTE ON COSTUME

    The dress of the young Venetian nobleman was a close-fitting doublet and breeches of some rich material, the breeches cut wide at the top and narrowing in at the knee, gold buttons, a small white ruff, and a high cap of stiff silk, satin, or velvet, adorned with one big jewel in front, or with a tiny garland wrought in metal-work, with precious stones. Sometimes doublet and breeches were slashed to show a lining of coloured taffetas. This was the gay apparel of early manhood; as he grew older, the Venetian generally chose to wear out of doors a long garment of fine black cloth faced with watered silk, and a little black brimless cap. The merchant princes of the city often wore a tunic reaching to the ground, with clasps and girdle of silk, and a short cloak. Shylock's " gaberdine " is a robe with long full sleeves cut open to show tightly-fitting undersleeves, and a broad sash-like belt. He must wear a yellow cap; Jessica a yellow veil—the Venetian law insisting on these distinctive features in the dress of Jewish men and women. As servant of Shylock, Launcelot should be plainly dressed in doublet and hose of russet brown or grey.

The appearance of the Duke, or Doge, was very splendid. His tunic, which reached the ground, and his trailing mantle were of velvet; he wore a short ermine cloak, just covering his shoulders, clasped with gold, and a velvet cap bent up behind in the form of a horn, and closed in a band of gold.

The fashion of what has come to be called the " Portia dress " is a becoming one: the bodice is pointed, the neck cut away in front, but not very low, the skirt full, and the ruff prettily shaped as a setting for the head. The Venetian lady wore a long veil, and carried a fan. She liked jewels—necklaces, bracelets, and ear-rings.

As jurisconsult, Portia would have worn a long robe, cut with open sleeves, and made of black cloth, velvet, or silk, and a black cap of similar material. Any modern academic gown will do for her disguise, if worn with a white neckcloth and the black cap.

SCENE I

A street in Venice.

[*Enter* ANTONIO, *a rich merchant of Venice, and*
SALARINO, *a young Venetian nobleman, walking
together.*]

   Ant. In sooth, I know not why I am so sad :
It wearies me ; you say it wearies you ;
But how I caught it, found it, or came by it,
What stuff 'tis made of, whereof it is born,
10 I am to learn ;
And such a want-wit sadness makes of me
That I have much ado to know myself.
   Sal. Your mind is tossing on the ocean ;
There, where your argosies with portly sail,
Like signiors and rich burghers of the flood,
Or, as it were, the pageants of the sea,
Do overpeer the petty traffickers,
That curtsy to them, do them reverence,
As they fly past them with their woven wings.
20   *Ant.* [*smiling and shaking his head*]. Believe me, no :
      I thank my fortune for it,
My ventures are not in one bottom trusted,
Therefore my merchandise makes me not sad.
   Sal. Here comes Bassanio, your most noble kins-
man,
Gratiano and Lorenzo. Fare ye well :
I leave you now with better company.   [*Exit.*

[*Enter* BASSANIO, LORENZO, *and* GRATIANO. BAS-
SANIO *is handsome and debonair. His dress is*
30   *perfect in every detail ; he has never been accus-*

---

6. *In sooth,* In truth.   14. *Argosies,* Great merchant ships.
16. *Pageants,* Shows.   17. *Petty traffickers,* Small cargo boats.
                22. *Bottom,* Ship.

tomed to counting the cost of things. LORENZO *is rather dreamy in appearance, and he carries a flower.* GRATIANO *is noisy and good-humoured, with merry eyes.* BASSANIO *goes at once to* ANTONIO'S *side, and the friends greet one another warmly.*]

Gra. You look not well, Signior Antonio ;
You have too much respect upon the world :
They lose it that do buy it with much care :
40 Believe me, you are marvellously changed.

Ant. [*gravely*]. I hold the world but as the world, Gratiano ;
A stage where every man must play his part,
And mine a sad one.

Gra. Let me play the fool :
With mirth and laughter let old wrinkles come,
And let my liver rather heat with wine
Than my heart cool with mortifying groans.
Why should a man, whose blood is warm within,
50 Sit like his grandsire cut in alabaster ?
Sleep when he wakes and creep into the jaundice
By being peevish ? I tell thee what, Antonio—
I love thee, and it is my love that speaks—
There are a sort of men whose visages
Do cream and mantle like a standing pond,
And do a wilful stillness entertain,
With purpose to be dress'd in an opinion
Of wisdom, gravity, profound conceit,
As who should say, " I am Sir Oracle,
60 And when I ope my lips let no dog bark ! "
Come, good Lorenzo. [*To* ANTONIO] Fare ye well awhile :
I'll end my exhortation after dinner.

38. *Respect,* Consideration.
48. *Mortifying,* Death-bringing. There was an old belief that
    when a man sighed deeply he lost a certain amount of
    vitality and so shortened his life.
58. *Conceit,* Understanding.

Lor. Well, we will leave you then till dinner-time :
I must be one of these same dumb wise men,
For Gratiano never lets me speak.

Gra. Well, keep me company but two years moe,
Thou shalt not know the sound of thine own tongue.

[*They go out laughing together, and the friends are
70   left alone.*

Ant. Is that anything now ?

Bass. Gratiano speaks an infinite deal of nothing,
more than any man in all Venice.   His reasons are as
two grains of wheat hid in two bushels of chaff : you
shall seek all day ere you find them, and when you
have them, they are not worth the search.

Ant. Well, tell me now what lady is the same
To whom you swore a secret pilgrimage,
That you to-day promised to tell me of ?

80   *Bass.* [*raptly and yet simply, without a trace of the
          man-of-the-world manner he sometimes assumes*].
          In Belmont is a lady richly left ;
And she is fair, and, fairer than that word,
Of wondrous virtues : sometimes from her eyes
I did receive fair speechless messages :
Her name is Portia, nothing undervalued
To Cato's daughter, Brutus' Portia :
Nor is the wide world ignorant of her worth,
For the four winds blow in from every coast
90 Renowned suitors, and her sunny locks
Hang on her temples like a golden fleece ;
Which makes her seat of Belmont Colchos' strand,
And many Jasons come in quest of her.

---

67. *Moe,* More.   75. *Ere,* Before.
87. *Brutus.*   A Roman patriot, who joined the conspiracy against
        Cæsar when convinced that the latter threatened the liberty
        of Rome.   His wife Portia proved her ability to share and
        keep his secret by giving herself a deep wound, of which she
        said nothing to him until it was healed.
93. *Jason.*   The hero who, with the help of the enchantress Medea,
        obtained the golden fleece from the grove in Colchis, where
        it was guarded by a sleepless dragon.

O my Antonio, had I but the means
To hold a rival place with one of them,
I have a mind presages me such thrift,
That I should questionless be fortunate !
    Ant. Thou know'st that all my fortunes are at sea ;
Neither have I money nor commodity
100 To raise a present sum : therefore go forth ;
Try what my credit can in Venice do :
That shall be rack'd even to the uttermost,
To furnish thee to Belmont, to fair Portia.
Go, presently inquire, and so will I,
Where money is, and I no question make
To have it of my trust or for my sake.
      [BASSANIO *takes him by the hand with an impulsive
        gesture of gratitude.*

CURTAIN

SCENE II

The same.

[*Enter* BASSANIO *with* SHYLOCK, *the Jew from whom
he proposes to borrow money on* ANTONIO'S *credit.*
SHYLOCK *leans on his staff, pondering, now and
then darting a glance at* BASSANIO, *as if he were
" sizing up " this young man and his friend, and
what worth they may prove to him.*]

    Shy. Three thousand ducats—well.
10   *Bass.* [*curtly, but controlling his impatience*]. Ay, sir,
for three months.
    Shy. For three months—well.

96. *Presages*, Foretells.   96. *Thrift*, Success, profit.
99. *Commodity*, Goods, article of merchandise.
104. *Presently*, At once.
9. *Ducat*, Coin worth 4*s*. 8*d*. in Venice.

Bass. For the which, as I told you, Antonio shall be bound.

Shy. Antonio shall become bound—well.

Bass. [*becoming exasperated*]. May you stead me ? will you pleasure me ? shall I know your answer ?

Shy. [*unmoved*]. Three thousand ducats, for three months, and Antonio bound.

20 *Bass.* Your answer to that.

Shy. [*thoughtfully*]. Antonio is a good man.

Bass. [*quickly*]. Have you heard any imputation to the contrary ?

Shy. O, no, no, no, no : my meaning in saying he is a good man is to have you understand me that he is sufficient. Yet his means are in supposition ; he hath an argosy bound to Tripolis, another to the Indies ; I understand, moreover, upon the Rialto, he hath a third at Mexico, a fourth for England, and other 30 ventures he hath, squandered abroad. But ships are but boards, sailors but men : there be land-rats and water-rats, land-thieves and water-thieves, I mean pirates, and then there is the peril of waters, winds, and rocks. [*Regards* BASSANIO *with a half-humorous cunning.*] The man is, notwithstanding, sufficient. Three thousand ducats ; I think I may take his bond.

Bass. Be assured you may.

Shy. I will be assured I may ; and, that I may be assured, I will bethink me. May I speak with 40 Antonio ?

Bass. If it please you to dine with us.

Shy. Yes, to smell pork ; to eat of the habitation which your prophet the Nazarite conjured the devil into. I will buy with you, sell with you, talk with you, walk with you, and so following, but I will not eat with you, drink with you, nor pray with you. [*Remains for a few seconds as if in thought, bowed over*

16. *Stead me*, Help me.
26. *Sufficient, i.e.* His financial position is secure.
28. *Rialto*, The Venetian Exchange.

his staff, then rouses himself, eyeing Bassanio *with the same half-humorous look.*] What news on the Rialto ?
50 Who is he comes here ?

[*Enter* Antonio.   Shylock's *expression changes for one of bitter contempt and hate.*]

Bass. [*confidently presenting his wealthy friend*]. This is Signior Antonio.
[Shylock *looks at him and looks away.*
Shy. [*aside*]. How like a fawning publican he looks !
I hate him for he is a Christian,
But more for that in low simplicity
60 He lends out money gratis and brings down
The rate of usance here with us in Venice.
If I can catch him once upon the hip,
I will feed fat the ancient grudge I bear him.
He hates our sacred nation, and he rails,
Even there where merchants most do congregate,
On me, my bargains, and my well-won thrift,
Which he calls interest.   Cursed be my tribe,
If I forgive him !
Bass.   Shylock, do you hear ?
70 *Shy.* [*turning with a change of tone*]. I am debating of my present store,
And, by the near guess of my memory,
I cannot instantly raise up the gross
Of full three thousand ducats.   What of that ?
Tubal, a wealthy Hebrew of my tribe,
Will furnish me.   But soft ! how many months
Do you desire ? [*Reflects, nodding his head, and then turns to* Antonio] Rest you fair, good signior ;
Your worship was the last man in our mouths.

---

56. *Publican,* The Roman tax-gatherer, hated by the Jews in the days of the New Testament.
60. *Gratis,* Free.   61. *Usance,* Usury, interest.
62. *Catch him on the hip,* Get the advantage of him, as in wrestling.

80   *Ant.* Well, Shylock, shall we be beholding to you ?
      Shy. [*glancing at him, and suddenly moved by his
            hatred to speak from his soul*]. Signior Antonio,
            many a time and oft
In the Rialto you have rated me
About my moneys and my usances :
Still have I borne it with a patient shrug,
For sufferance is the badge of all our tribe.
You call me misbeliever, cut-throat dog,
And spit upon my Jewish gaberdine,
90 And all for use of that which is mine own.
Well then, it now appears you need my help :
Go to, then, you come to me, and you say,
" Shylock, we would have moneys " : [*with gathering
            passion*] *you* say so ;
You, that did void your rheum upon my beard
And foot me as you spurn a stranger cur
Over your threshold : moneys is your suit.
What should I say to you ? Should I not say,
" Hath a dog money ? is it possible
100 A cur can lend three thousand ducats ? " Or,
Shall I bend low and in a bondman's key,
With bated breath and whispering humbleness,
Say this :
      [*In bitter imitation of the fawning, submissive
            manner of the downtrodden Oriental.*
" Fair sir, you spit on me on Wednesday last ;
You spurn'd me such a day ; another time
You call'd me dog ; and for these courtesies
I'll lend you thus much moneys."
110   *Ant.* [*with a kind of hard anger, utterly untouched by
            the passion of the Jew's outburst*]. I am as like
            to call thee so again,
To spit on thee again, to spurn thee too.
If thou wilt lend this money, lend it not
As to thy friends ; for when did friendship take

87. *Sufferance*, Endurance.

A breed for barren metal of his friend ?
But lend it rather to thine enemy,
Who if he break, thou mayst with better face
Exact the penalty.

120   *Shy.* [*with a complete change of manner*]. Why, look
      you, how you storm !
I would be friends with you and have your love,
Forget the shames that you have stain'd me with,
Supply your present wants and take no doit
Of usance for my moneys, and you'll not hear me :
This is kind I offer.

   Bass. [*eagerly*]. This were kindness.

   Shy. [*watching* ANTONIO'S *face*]. This kindness
will I show.

130 Go with me to a notary, seal me there
Your single bond ; and, in a merry sport,
If you repay me not on such a day,
In such a place, such sum or sums as are
Express'd in the condition, let the forfeit
Be nominated for an equal pound
Of your fair flesh, to be cut off and taken
In what part of your body pleaseth me.

    [*Regards* ANTONIO *with his half-humorous look,*
       appearing an eccentric old fellow who has taken
140   *a crazy though harmless enough notion into his*
       head, and is anxious to have his whim gratified.

   Ant. [*as if amused*]. Content, i' faith : I'll seal to
    such a bond
And say there is much kindness in the Jew.

   Bass. [*with sudden vehemence*]. You shall not seal to
    such a bond for me :
I'll rather dwell in my necessity.

    [*The Jew darts a glance at him, and looks down.*

   Ant. Why, fear not, man ; I will not forfeit it :
150 Within these two months, that's a month before

---

116. *A breed, i.e.* Interest arising from money lent.
118. *Break, i.e.* Fail to pay.   124. *Doit,* Farthing.

This bond expires, I do expect return
Of thrice three times the value of this bond.
    Shy. [*shaking his head, half amused, half exasperated*].
        O father Abram, what these Christians are,
Whose own hard dealings teaches them suspect
The thoughts of others! [*To* BASSANIO] Pray you,
        tell me this ;
If he should break his day, what should I gain
By the exaction of the forfeiture ?
160 A pound of man's flesh taken from a man
Is not so estimable, profitable neither,
As flesh of muttons, beefs, or goats.   I say,
To buy his favour, I extend this friendship :
If he will take it, so ; if not, adieu ;
And, for my love, I pray you wrong me not.
    Ant. Yes, Shylock, I will seal unto this bond.
    Shy. Then meet me forthwith at the notary's ;
Give him direction for this merry bond,
And I will go and purse the ducats straight,
170 See to my house, left in the fearful guard
Of an unthrifty knave, and presently
I will be with you.
    Ant. [*in the friendliest way*]. Hie thee, gentle Jew.
                                    [*Exit* SHYLOCK.
The Hebrew will turn Christian : he grows kind.
    Bass. [*still ill at ease*]. I like not fair terms and a
        villain's mind.
    Ant. [*rallying him*]. Come on : in this there can be
        no dismay ;
180 My ships come home a month before the day.
                                    [*Exeunt.*

CURTAIN

161. *Estimable*, Valuable.   171. *Knave*, Boy.

SCENE III

Before SHYLOCK'S *house, which is supposed to be left of the stage.*

[*Enter* SHYLOCK, *followed by his servant,* LAUNCELOT GOBBO, *a youth with a broad comical face and wispy straw-coloured hair.*]

Shy. [*rapping with his staff, and getting no reply*]. What, Jessica! What, Jessica! Why, Jessica, I say!

10 *Laun.* [*imitating him*]. Why, Jessica!
Shy. Who bids thee call? I do not bid thee call.
Laun. [*injured*]. Your worship was wont to tell me that I could do nothing without bidding.

[*Enter* JESSICA, *pretty and sullen.* LAUNCELOT *makes secret signs to her, trying to deliver a letter from* LORENZO, *which* SHYLOCK *must not see. For the time being the attempt is foiled.*]

Jess. Call you? what is your will?
Shy. I am bid forth to supper, Jessica:
20 There are my keys. [*As if to himself*] But wherefore should I go?
I am not bid for love; they flatter me:
But yet I'll go in hate, to feed upon
The prodigal Christian. Jessica, my girl,
Look to the house. [*She takes the keys.*] I am right loath to go:
There is some ill a-brewing towards my rest,
For I did dream of money-bags to-night.
Laun. I beseech you, sir, go; my new master doth
30 expect your reproach.
Shy. [*grimly*]. So do I his.
Laun. [*eagerly*]. An they have conspired together,

I will not say you shall see a masque ; but if you do,
then it was not for nothing that my nose fell a-bleed-
ing on Black Monday last at six o'clock i' the morning,
falling out that year on Ash Wednesday was four year,
in the afternoon.

    Shy. [*suspicious at once*]. What, are there masques ?
        Hear you me, Jessica :
40 Lock up my doors ; and when you hear the drum
And the vile squealing of the wry-neck'd fife,
Clamber not you up to the casements then,
Nor thrust your head into the public street
To gaze on Christian fools with varnish'd faces,
But stop my house's ears, I mean my casements :
Let not the sound of shallow foppery enter
My sober house. By Jacob's staff, I swear
I have no mind of feasting forth to-night :
But I will go. [*To* LAUNCELOT] Go you before me,
50   sirrah ;
Say I will come.
    Laun. [*with such alacrity as to awake* SHYLOCK'S
suspicions once more]. I will go before, sir. [*Aside to*
JESSICA, *to whom he contrives to give the letter*] Mistress,
look out at window, for all this ;
        There will come a Christian by,
        Will be worth a Jewess' eye.   [*Exit.*
    Shy. What says that fool of Hagar's offspring, ha ?
    Jes. [*hiding the letter*]. His words were " Farewell,
60   mistress," nothing else.
    Shy. The patch is kind enough, but a huge feeder ;
Snail-slow in profit, and he sleeps by day
More than the wild cat ; drones hive not with me :
Therefore I part with him, and part with him
To one that I would have him help to waste
His borrow'd purse. Well, Jessica, go in :
Perhaps I will return immediately :

---

58. *Hagar's offspring,* The child of the bondwoman, not the free.
61. *Patch,* Fool.

Do as I bid you ; shut doors after you :
Fast bind, fast find :
70 A proverb never stale in thrifty mind.

> [*She goes in, and he slowly departs, once looking back as if he had almost made up his mind to return. Music and laughter. The maskers, in fantastically coloured and decorated dominoes, and black masks, dance across the stage, brandishing torches, scattering flowers.*

[*Then enter* GRATIANO *and* SALARINO.]

Gra. This is the pent-house under which Lorenzo
Desired us to make stand.
80   *Sal.*   His hour is almost past.
Gra. And it is marvel he out-dwells his hour,
For lovers ever run before the clock.

[*Enter* LORENZO.]

Lor. Sweet friends, your patience for my long abode;
Not I, but my affairs, have made you wait :
When you shall please to play the thieves for wives,
I'll watch as long for you then.   Approach ;
[*Amused at the notion*] Here dwells my father Jew.
    [*Knocking*] Ho ! who's within ?
90   *Jessica's voice* [*as if from the window above*]. Who
        are you ?   Tell me, for more certainty,
Albeit I'll swear that I do know your tongue.
Lor. Lorenzo, and thy love.
Jes. Lorenzo, certain ; and my love indeed.
Here, catch this casket ; it is worth the pains.
                    [*She throws down a casket of gold.*
Lor. Descend, for you must be my torch-bearer.
Jes. I will make fast the doors, and gild myself
With some more ducats, and be with you straight.
100   *Gra.* [*approvingly*]. Now, by my hood, a Gentile,
        and no Jew,
    Lor. Beshrew me but I love her heartily.

[*Enter* JESSICA, *wrapped in a cloak, carrying*
a bag of gold.]

What, art thou come ?   On, gentlemen, away !
Our masquing mates by this time for us stay.
      [*They go out, and the maskers once more pass danc-*
         ing over the stage, in a drift of colour and music.

110 [*When they have gone, and the sound of their revelry*
         has died away, enter SHYLOCK, *slowly, head bent,*
         a dark and lonely figure.   He taps with his staff
         on the door of the house.   There is no answer.   He
         taps again.]

CURTAIN

SCENE IV

A street in Venice.

[*Enter* SALARINO *and* SALANIO.]

Salar. Why, man, I saw Bassanio under sail :
With him is Gratiano gone along ;
And in their ship I am sure Lorenzo is not.
   Salan. The villain Jew with outcries raised the duke,
Who went with him to search Bassanio's ship.
   Salar. He came too late, the ship was under sail :
10 But there the duke was given to understand
That in a gondola were seen together
Lorenzo and his amorous Jessica :
Besides, Antonio certified the duke
They were not with Bassanio in his ship.
   Salan. [*gravely*]. Let good Antonio look he keep his
      day,

------

112. *On the door :* Or on the floor if the entrance to his house is not
         represented.   What is wanted is the illusion of the unanswered
         knock.

Or he shall pay for this.

    Salar.   Marry, well remember'd.

I reason'd with a Frenchman yesterday,

20 Who told me, in the narrow seas that part

The French and English, there miscarried

A vessel of our country richly fraught :

I thought upon Antonio when he told me,

And wish'd in silence that it were not his.

[*Enter* SHYLOCK. *He looks haggard and tortured ; his passionate hatred of the Christians is now manifest in every gesture and glance.*]

    Salan. How now, Shylock ! what news among the merchants ?

30   *Shy.* [*in bitter fury*]. You knew, none so well, none so well as you, of my daughter's flight.

    Salar. [*amused*]. That's certain : I, for my part, knew the tailor that made the wings she flew withal.

    Shy. [*as if to himself*]. My own flesh and blood to rebel !

    Salar. There is more difference between thy flesh and hers than between jet and ivory ; more between your bloods than there is between red wine and Rhenish. But tell us, do you hear whether Antonio

40 have had any loss at sea or no ?

    Shy. There I have another bad match : a bankrupt, a prodigal, who dare scarce show his head on the Rialto : a beggar, that was used to come so smug upon the mart ; [*With dreadful significance*] let him look to his bond : he was wont to call me usurer ; let him look to his bond : he was wont to lend money for a Christian courtesy ; let him look to his bond.

    [*The expresssion of rather forced amusement on the faces of the two young men changes, and is*

50   *succeeded by apprehension.*

---

19. *Reason'd*, Talked.   21. *Miscarried*, Perished.
22. *Fraught*, Laden.   43. *Smug*, Spruce.

Salar. Why, I am sure, if he forfeit, thou wilt not take his flesh : what's that good for ?

Shy. [*with a kind of grim humour*]. To bait fish withal : if it will feed nothing else, it will feed my revenge. [*With gathering passion*] He hath disgraced me, and hindered me half a million ; laughed at my losses, mocked at my gains, scorned my nation, thwarted my bargains, cooled my friends, heated my enemies ; and what's his reason ? I am a Jew. Hath 60 not a Jew eyes ? hath not a Jew hands, organs, dimensions, senses, affections, passions ? fed with the same food, hurt with the same weapons, subject to the same diseases, healed by the same means, warmed and cooled by the same winter and summer, as a Christian is ? If you prick us, do we not bleed ? if you tickle us, do we not laugh ? if you poison us, do we not die ? and if you wrong us, shall we not revenge ? If we are like you in the rest, we will resemble you in that. If a Jew wrong a Christian, what is his humility ? 70 Revenge. If a Christian wrong a Jew, what should his sufferance be by Christian example ? Why, revenge. The villainy you teach me, I will execute, and it shall go hard but I will better the instruction.

[*The young men look at one another in consternation, which they unsuccessfully try to hide.*

[*Enter a* Servant *from* ANTONIO.]

Serv. Gentlemen, my master Antonio is at his house and desires to speak with you both.

Salar. We have been up and down to seek him.

80   [*Exit* Servant.

[*Enter* TUBAL.]

Salan. [*somewhat recovering himself*]. Here comes another of the tribe : a third cannot be matched, unless the devil himself turn Jew.   [*They go out.*

71. *Sufferance,* Endurance.

Shy. [*eagerly laying hold of* TUBAL *by the sleeve*]. How now, Tubal! what news from Genoa? hast thou found my daughter?

Tub. I often came where I did hear of her, but cannot find her.

90 *Shy.* [*for a moment the rich and avaricious money-lender robbed, and angered by his losses*]. Why, there, there, there, there! a diamond gone, cost me two thousand ducats in Frankfort! The curse never fell upon our nation till now; I never felt it till now; two thousand ducats in that, and other—precious, precious jewels. [*Suddenly possessed with anger and the desire of vengeance*] I would my daughter were dead at my foot, and the jewels in her ear! would she were hearsed at my foot, and the ducats in her coffin!
100 [*Wearily, as the reaction following the strength of the fury urging the terrible wish creeps over him*] No news of them? Why so: and I know not what's spent in the search; why, thou loss upon loss! the thief gone with so much, and so much to find the thief; and no satisfaction, no revenge: [*In the utter desolation of misfortune*] nor no ill luck stirring but what lights on my shoulder; no sighs but of my breathing, no tears but of my shedding.

[*Turns from* TUBAL, *and stands as if in a trance of grief.*
110

Tub. Yes, other men have ill luck too: Antonio, as as I heard in Genoa——

Shy. [*rousing himself, in a sort of delirium of eagerness*]. What, what, what? ill luck, ill luck?

Tub. Hath an argosy cast away, coming from Tripolis.

Shy. [*lifting his hands*]. I thank God, I thank God. [*Eagerly and fearfully*] Is't true, is't true?

Tub. I spoke with some of the sailors that escaped 120 the wreck.

Shy. I thank thee, good Tubal: good news, good news! ha, ha! where? in Genoa?

Tub. Your daughter spent in Genoa, as I heard, in one night fourscore ducats.

Shy. Thou stickest a dagger in me : I shall never see my gold again : fourscore ducats at a sitting ! fourscore ducats !

Tub. There came divers of Antonio's creditors in my company to Venice, that swear he cannot choose
130 but break.

Shy. [*again the incarnation of vengeance*]. I am very glad of it : I'll plague him ; I'll torture him :—I am glad of it.

Tub. One of them showed me a ring that he had of your daughter for a monkey.

Shy. Out upon her ! Thou torturest me, Tubal : it was my turquoise ; I had it of Leah when I was a bachelor : I would not have given it for a wilderness of monkeys.

140 *Tub.* But Antonio is certainly undone.

Shy. Nay, that's true, that's very true. Go, Tubal, fee me an officer ; bespeak him a fortnight before. I will have the heart of him, if he forfeit ; for, were he out of Venice, I can make what merchandise I will. Go, go, Tubal, and meet me at our synagogue ; go, good Tubal ; at our synagogue, Tubal.

[TUBAL *goes out.* SHYLOCK *stands silent, brooding over his wrongs and his vengeance.*

CURTAIN

SCENE V

A room in PORTIA'S *house at Belmont.* PORTIA *sits on a seat left of the stage with* BALTHASAR *in attendance ;* BASSANIO *is at her feet. Her musicians stand before her ;* GRATIANO *and* NERISSA *are in the background. Right of the stage is a table, with an inkstand of metal, and a quill pen. The curtain rises to soft music, and the musicians sing :*

> Tell me where is fancy bred,
> Or in the heart or in the head ?
> How begot, how nourishèd ?
> Reply, reply.
> It is engender'd in the eyes,
> With gazing fed ; and fancy dies
> In the cradle where it lies.
> Let us all ring fancy's knell :
> I'll begin it—Ding, dong, bell.

All. Ding, dong, bell.

[*As the music dies away, enter* SALANIO.]

Bass. [*going towards him and greeting him*]. Welcome hither ;
If that the youth of my new interest here
Have power to bid you welcome. [*To* PORTIA] By your leave,
I bid my very friend and countryman,
Sweet Portia, welcome.

Por. [*greeting* SALANIO]. So do I, my lord :
He is entirely welcome.

Salan. Signor Antonio
Commends him to you. [*Gives* BASSANIO *a letter.*

[BASSANIO *tears open the letter ;* GRATIANO *goes up to* SALANIO.

Gra. Your hand, Salanio : what's the news from Venice ?
How doth that royal merchant, good Antonio ?
I know he will be glad of our success ;
We are the Jasons, we have won the fleece.

Sal. I would you had won the fleece that he hath lost.

---

9. *Fancy,* Love.   25. *Very friend,* True friend.

40   *Por.* [*watching* BASSANIO *as he reads the letter*]. There
            are some shrewd contents in yon same paper,
That steals the colour from Bassanio's cheek :
Some dear friend dead ; else nothing in the world
Could turn so much the constitution
Of any constant man.   What, worse and worse !
With leave, Bassanio ; I am half yourself,
And I must freely have the half of anything
That this same paper brings you.
            Bass.   O sweet Portia,
50 When I did first impart my love to you,
I freely told you, all the wealth I had
Ran in my veins, I was a gentleman ;
But I am worse than nothing ; for indeed
I have engaged myself to a dear friend,
Engaged my friend to a mere enemy,
To feed my means.   [*Gives her the letter.*]   But is it
            true, Salanio ?
Have all his ventures failed ?
            Sal.   Each one, my lord.
60   *Por.* [*looking up from the letter*]. Is it your dear friend
            that is thus in trouble ?
Bass. The dearest friend to me, the kindest man,
The best-condition'd and unwearied spirit
In doing courtesies, and one in whom
The ancient Roman honour more appears
Than any that draws breath in Italy.
    Por. What sum owes he the Jew ?
    Bass. For me three thousand ducats.
    Por.   What, no more ?
70 Pay him six thousand, and deface the bond ;
Double six thousand, and then treble that,
Before a friend of this description
Shall lose a hair thorough Bassanio's fault.
You must away to Venice to your friend ;

41. *Shrewd*, Evil.   45. *Constant*, Normally self-possessed.
54. *Engaged*, Pledged.
55. *Mere*, Pure, undiluted ; hence thorough, unqualified.

O love, dispatch all business, and be gone !
   Bass. Since I have your good leave to go away,
I will make haste : but, till I come again,
No bed shall e'er be guilty of my stay,
No rest be interposer 'twixt us twain.

80   [*He bids her farewell, and* GRATIANO *takes his leave*
       of NERISSA. *They go out, followed by* SALANIO.
   Por. [*summoning her attendant* BALTHASAR]. Now,
      Balthasar,
Prepare thee for a journey ; I'll write a letter,
And use thou all the endeavour of a man
In speed to Padua : see thou render it
Into my cousin's hand, Doctor Bellario ;
And, look, what notes and garments he doth give thee,
Bring them, I pray thee, with imagined speed
90 Unto the tranect, to the common ferry
Which trades to Venice. Waste no time in words,
Make ready now : I shall be there before thee.
   Balth. Madam, I go with all convenient speed.

                             [*Exit.*

   Por. Come on, Nerissa ; I have work in hand
That you yet know not of : we'll see our husbands
Before they think of us.
   Ner.   Shall they see us ?
   Por. [*with humorous delight in her plan*]. They shall,
100   Nerissa ; but in such a habit,
That they shall think we are accomplished
With that we lack. I hold thee any wager,
When we are both accoutred like young men,
I'll prove the prettier fellow of the two,
And wear my dagger with the braver grace,
And speak between the change of man and boy
With a reed voice, and turn two mincing steps
Into a manly stride, and speak of frays
Like a fine bragging youth, and tell quaint lies,

---

90. *Tranect.* Probably for traject, one of the traghetti, or ferries of
    Venice.
103. *Accoutred,* Arrayed.   109. *Quaint,* Ingenious.

110 How honourable ladies sought my love,
Which I denying, they fell sick and died ;
I could not do withal ; then I'll repent,
And wish, for all that, that I had not kill'd them ;
And twenty of these puny lies I'll tell,
That men shall swear I have discontinued school
Above a twelvemonth.   I have within my mind
A thousand raw tricks of these bragging Jacks,
Which I will practise.   I'll write my letter,

　　　[*Seats herself at the table and takes paper and a pen.*
120 And I will tell you all my whole device
When I am in my coach ; and therefore haste away,
For we must measure twenty miles to-day.

　　　[NERISSA *goes out ;* PORTIA *begins to write quickly
　　　　and intently.*

CURTAIN

SCENE VI

*A court of justice at Venice.   At the back of the stage,
on a low dais, sits the* DUKE, *behind a table covered with
a scarlet or black cloth.   An* Attendant *stands on either
side of him.   At a small table, before the dais, is a clerk,
writing.   To the right of the stage are* ANTONIO, BAS-
SANIO, *and* GRATIANO. (*Magnificoes of Venice may
occupy the dais with the* DUKE, *and spectators may be
introduced if the stage is a large one and there are plenty
10 of performers.*)

Duke. What, is Antonio here ?
Ant. [*coming forward*]. Ready, so please your grace.
Duke. Go one, and call the Jew into the court.
Gra. He is ready at the door : he comes, my lord.

──────────

113. *I could not do withal,* I could not help it.

[*Enter* SHYLOCK. *He looks haggard and worn, but he walks with upright, almost triumphant bearing.*]

Duke. Make room, and let him stand before our
  face.

[*In a grave, reasonable tone of voice*] Shylock, the
20 world thinks, and I think so too,
That thou but lead'st this fashion of thy malice
To the last hour of act : and then 'tis thought
Thou'lt show thy mercy and remorse more strange
Than is thy strange apparent cruelty :
And where thou now exact'st the penalty,
Which is a pound of this poor merchant's flesh,
Thou wilt not only loose the forfeiture,
But, touch'd with human gentleness and love,
Forgive a moiety of the principal,
30 Glancing an eye of pity on his losses.
We all expect a gentle answer, Jew.

  Shy. I have possess'd your grace of what I purpose ;
And by our holy Sabbath have I sworn
To have the due and forfeit of my bond :
If you deny it, let the danger light
Upon your charter and your city's freedom.
You'll ask me, why I rather choose to have
A weight of carrion flesh than to receive
Three thousand ducats : I'll not answer that :
40 But, say, it is my humour : is it answer'd ?
What if my house be troubled with a rat,
And I be pleased to give ten thousand ducats
To have it baned ? What, are you answer'd yet ?
Some men there are love not a gaping pig ;
Some, that are mad if they behold a cat ;
Some, when they hear the bagpipe : now, for your
  answer :

23. *Remorse*, Compassion.   29. *Moiety*, Portion.
32. *Possess'd*, Informed.
36. *Charter*. Shakespeare is thinking of the royal charter by which
  an English city was given the right to administer justice.
  Venice was at this time an independent sovereign state.

As there is no firm reason to be render'd,
Why he cannot abide a gaping pig ;
50 Why he, a harmless necessary cat ;
So can I give no reason, nor I will not,
More than a lodged hate and a certain loathing
I bear Antonio, that I follow thus
A losing suit against him.   Are you answer'd ?

Bass. [*passionately*]. This is no answer, thou un-
feeling man,
To excuse the current of thy cruelty.

Shy. I am not bound to please thee with my
answers.

60   *Bass.* Do all men kill the things they do not love ?

Shy. Hates any man the thing he would not kill ?

Bass. Every offence is not a hate at first.

Shy. What, wouldst thou have a serpent sting thee
twice ?

Ant. I pray you, think you question with the
Jew :
You may as well go stand upon the beach
And bid the main flood bate his usual height ;
You may as well use question with the wolf
70 Why he has made the ewe bleat for the lamb ;
You may as well forbid the mountain pines
To wag their high tops and to make no noise,
When they are fretted with the gusts of heaven ;
You may as well do anything most hard,
As seek to soften that—than which what's harder ?—
His Jewish heart : therefore, I do beseech you,
Make no more offers, use no further means,
But with all brief and plain conveniency
Let me have judgment and the Jew his will.

80   *Bass.* [*holding out the money*]. For thy three thousand ducats here is six.

Shy. [*not even looking at it*]. If every ducat in six
thousand ducats
Were in six parts and every part a ducat,
I would not draw them ; I would have my bond.

Duke. How shalt thou hope for mercy, rendering none?

Shy. What judgment shall I dread, doing no wrong?
90 The pound of flesh, which I demand of him,
Is dearly bought; 'tis mine and I will have it.
If you deny me, fie upon your law!
There is no force in the decrees of Venice.
I stand for judgment: answer; shall I have it?

Duke. Upon my power I may dismiss this court,
Unless Bellario, a learned doctor,
Whom I have sent for to determine this,
Come here to-day.

Clerk. My lord, here stays without
100 A messenger with letters from the doctor,
New come from Padua.

Duke. Bring us the letters; call the messenger.

[*Exit an* Attendant.

Bass. Good cheer, Antonio! What, man, courage yet!
The Jew shall have my flesh, blood, bones, and all,
Ere thou shalt lose for me one drop of blood.

Ant. I am a tainted wether of the flock,
Meetest for death: the weakest kind of fruit
110 Drops earliest to the ground; and so let me:
You cannot better be employed, Bassanio,
Than to live still and write mine epitaph.

[*Enter* NERISSA, *dressed like a lawyer's clerk.*]

Duke. Came you from Padua, from Bellario?

Ner. From both, my lord. Bellario greets your grace.

[*She gives the* DUKE *a letter. Meanwhile* SHY-
LOCK, *who seems unconscious of the new-comer,
sharpens his long thin knife on the sole of his
shoe.*

20 *Bass.* [*with a kind of horror*]. Why dost thou whet thy knife so earnestly?

(2,799)

10

Shy. To cut the forfeiture from that bankrupt there.
Gra. [*beside himself with anger and dismay*]. Not
    on thy sole, but on thy soul, harsh Jew,
Thou makest thy knife keen ; but no metal can,
No, not the hangman's axe, bear half the keenness
Of thy sharp envy.   Can no prayers pierce thee ?
    Shy. No, none that thou hast wit enough to make.
130   *Gra.* O, be thou damn'd, inexecrable dog !
And for thy life let justice be accused.
Thou almost makest me hold opinion
That souls of animals infuse themselves
Into the trunks of men : for thy desires
Are wolvish, bloody, starved, and ravenous.
    Shy. [*quite unmoved*]. Till thou canst rail the seal
        from off my bond,
Thou but offend'st thy lungs to speak so loud :
Repair thy wit, good youth, or it will fall
140 To cureless ruin.   I stand here for law.
    Duke. This letter from Bellario doth commend
A young and learned doctor to our court.
Where is he ?
    Ner.   He attendeth here hard by,
To know your answer, whether you'll admit him.
    Duke. With all my heart.
        [*An* Attendant *goes out, and ushers in* PORTIA,
            dressed like a doctor of laws.
                        Came you from old Bellario ?
150   *Por.* [*bowing*]. I did, my lord.
    Duke.   You are welcome ; take your place.
Are you acquainted with the difference
That holds this present question in the court ?
    Por. I am informed throughly of the cause.
Which is the merchant here, and which the Jew ?
    Duke. Antonio and old Shylock, both stand forth.
    Por. Is your name Shylock ?
    Shy.   · Shylock is my name.
    Por. Of a strange nature is the suit you follow ;
160 Yet in such rule that the Venetian law

Cannot impugn you as you do proceed.
You stand within his danger, do you not ?

Ant. Ay, so he says.

Por. Do you confess the bond ?

Ant. I do.

Por. [*turning to* SHYLOCK]. Then must the Jew be
    merciful.

Shy. On what compulsion must I ? tell me that.

Por. The quality of mercy is not strain'd ;
170 It droppeth as the gentle rain from heaven
Upon the place beneath ; it is twice blest ;
It blesseth him that gives and him that takes :
'Tis mightiest in the mightiest : it becomes
The thronèd monarch better than his crown ;
His sceptre shows the force of temporal power,
The attribute to awe and majesty,
Wherein doth sit the dread and fear of kings ;
But mercy is above this sceptred sway :
It is enthronèd in the hearts of kings,
180 It is an attribute to God himself ;
And earthly power doth then show likest God's,
When mercy seasons justice. Therefore, Jew,
Though justice be thy plea, consider this,
That, in the course of justice, none of us
Should see salvation : we do pray for mercy ;
And that same prayer doth teach us all to render
The deeds of mercy. I have spoke thus much
To mitigate the justice of thy plea ;
Which if thou follow, this strict court of Venice
190 Must needs give sentence 'gainst the merchant there.

Shy. [*unmoved by this plea for mercy as he was by the
    offer of the ducats*]. My deeds upon my head ! I
    crave the law,
The penalty and forfeit of my bond.

Por. Is he not able to discharge the money ?

---

161. *Impugn,* Call in question.
162. *Danger.* To stand within a man's danger is to be in his power.

Bass. [*eagerly*]. Yes, here I tender it for him in the
       court ;
Yea, twice the sum : if that will not suffice,
I will be bound to pay it ten times o'er,
200 On forfeit of my hands, my head, my heart :
If this will not suffice, it must appear
That malice bears down truth.   And I beseech you,
Wrest once the law to your authority :
To do a great right, do a little wrong,
And curb this cruel devil of his will.

Por. It must not be ; there is no power in Venice
Can alter a decree established :
'Twill be recorded for a precedent,
And many an error by the same example
210 Will rush into the state : it cannot be.

Shy. [*exulting*]. A Daniel come to judgment ! yea, a
       Daniel !
O wise young judge, how I do honour thee !

Por. I pray you, let me look upon the bond.

Shy. Here 'tis, most reverend doctor, here it is.
                      [*Thrusts it into her hands.*

Por. [*glancing over it, and then regarding him*]. Shy-
       lock, there's thrice thy money offer'd thee.

Shy. [*lifting his hands*]. An oath, an oath, I have an
220   oath in heaven :
[*With a kind of humour*] Shall I lay perjury upon my
       soul ?
No, not for Venice.

Por.   Why, this bond is forfeit ;
And lawfully by this the Jew may claim
A pound of flesh, to be by him cut off
Nearest the merchant's heart.   [*To* SHYLOCK, *plead-
       ing with him for the last time*] Be merciful :
Take thrice thy money ; bid me tear the bond.
230   [*Holds it as if about to do so.*

Shy. [*taking it from her*]. When it is paid according
       to the tenour.
It doth appear you are a worthy judge ;

You know the law, your exposition
Hath been most sound : I charge you by the law,
Whereof you are a well-deserving pillar,
Proceed to judgment : by my soul I swear
There is no power in the tongue of man
To alter me : I stay here on my bond.

240   *Ant.* Most heartily I do beseech the court
To give the judgment.

   Por. [*with the dreadful solemnity of one passing
      sentence of death*]. Why then, thus it is :
You must prepare your bosom for his knife.

   Shy. [*no longer imperturbable, as he has been during
      most of the trial, but trembling with excitement*].
      O noble judge ! O excellent young man !

   Por. For the intent and purpose of the law
Hath full relation to the penalty,
250 Which here appeareth due upon the bond.

   Shy. 'Tis very true : O wise and upright judge !
How much more elder art thou than thy looks !

   Por. Therefore lay bare your bosom.

   Shy.   Ay, his breast :
So says the bond : doth it not, noble judge ?
" Nearest his heart " : those are the very words.

   Por. It is so. Are there balance here to weigh
The flesh ?

   Shy.   I have them ready.

260   *Por.* [*gravely and pitifully*]. Have by some surgeon,
    Shylock, on your charge,
To stop his wounds, lest he do bleed to death.

   Shy. Is it so nominated in the bond ?
                     [*Searches it as if to find out*

   Por. It is not so express'd : but what of that ?
'Twere good you do as much for charity.

   Shy. [*still examining his bond*]. I cannot find it ; 'tis
    not in the bond.

   Por. You, merchant, have you anything to say ?

270   *Ant.* But little : I am arm'd and well prepared.
Give me your hand, Bassanio, fare you well !

Grieve not that I am fallen to this for you :
Commend me to your honourable wife :
Tell her the process of Antonio's end ;
Say how I loved you, speak me fair in death ;
And, when the tale is told, bid her be judge
Whether Bassanio had not once a love.
Repent but you that you shall lose your friend,
And he repents not that he pays your debt :
280 For if the Jew do cut but deep enough,
I'll pay it instantly with all my heart.

   Bass. [*impulsively, almost overcome with his grief*].
      Antonio, I am married to a wife
Which is as dear to me as life itself ;
But life itself, my wife, and all the world,
Are not with me esteem'd above thy life :
I would lose all, ay, sacrifice them all
Here to this devil, to deliver you.

   Por. Your wife would give you little thanks for
290   that,
If she were by, to hear you make the offer.

   Gra. [*not to be outdone*]. I have a wife, whom, I pro-
     test, I love :
I would she were in heaven, so she could
Entreat some power to change this currish Jew.

   Ner. 'Tis well you offer it behind her back ;
The wish would else make an unquiet house.

   Shy. [*aside*]. These be the Christian husbands. I
     have a daughter ;
300 Would any of the stock of Barabbas
Had been her husband rather than a Christian !
[*Aloud*] We trifle time : I pray thee, pursue sentence.

   Por. [*solemnly*]. A pound of that same merchant's
     flesh is thine :
The court awards it, and the law doth give it.

   Shy. Most rightful judge !

   Por. And you must cut this flesh from off his
     breast :
The law allows it, and the court awards it.

310   *Shy.* Most learnèd judge! A sentence! Come,
      prepare!

      [ANTONIO *bares his bosom for the knife. An*
        Attendant *bandages his eyes; two more lead*
        BASSANIO *aside.* SHYLOCK *approaches his*
        victim, when PORTIA, *stepping forward, stays*
        his hand.

  Por. Tarry a little, there is something else.
This bond doth give thee here no jot of blood;
The words expressly are " a pound of flesh ":
320 Take then thy bond, take thou thy pound of flesh;
But in the cutting it, if thou dost shed
One drop of Christian blood, thy lands and goods
Are, by the laws of Venice, confiscate
Unto the state of Venice.

  Gra. [*at once realizing that* PORTIA *has played a*
    trump card]. O upright judge! Mark, Jew: O
    learnèd judge.

  Shy. [*slowly*]. Is that the law?   [*Drops his knife.*

  Por.   Thyself shalt see the act:
330 For, as thou urgest justice, be assured
Thou shalt have justice, more than thou desirest.

  Gra. O learnèd judge! Mark, Jew: a learnèd
    judge!

  Shy. [*no longer the incarnation of vengeance, but the*
    astute money-lender]. I take this offer, then;
    pay the bond thrice
And let the Christian go.

  Bass. [*eagerly*].   Here is the money.

  Por. [*restraining him*]. Soft!
340 The Jew shall have all justice; soft! no haste:
He shall have nothing but the penalty.

  Gra. O Jew! an upright judge, a learnèd judge!

  Por. Therefore prepare thee to cut off the flesh.
Shed thou no blood, nor cut thou less nor more
But just a pound of flesh: if thou tak'st more
Or less than a just pound, be it but so much
As makes it light or heavy in the substance

Or the division of the twentieth part
Of one poor scruple, nay, if the scale do turn
350 But in the estimation of a hair,
Thou diest, and all thy goods are confiscate.

    Gra. A second Daniel, a Daniel, Jew !
Now, infidel, I have thee on the hip.

    Por. Why doth the Jew pause ? take thy forfeiture.

    Shy. [*desperately*]. Give me my principal, and let
      me go.

    Bass. I have it ready for thee ; here it is.

    Por. He hath refused it in the open court :
He shall have merely justice and his bond.

360   *Gra.* A Daniel, still say I, a second Daniel !
I thank thee, Jew, for teaching me that word.

    Shy. [*in a trembling voice*]. Shall I not have barely
      my principal ?

    Por. Thou shalt have nothing but the forfeiture,
To be so taken at thy peril, Jew.

    Shy. Why, then the devil give him good of it !
I'll stay no longer question.

    Por.   Tarry, Jew :
The law hath yet another hold on you.
370 It is enacted in the laws of Venice,
If it be proved against an alien
That by direct or indirect attempts
He seek the life of any citizen,
The party 'gainst the which he doth contrive
Shall seize one half his goods ; the other half
Comes to the privy coffer of the state ;
And the offender's life lies in the mercy
Of the duke only, 'gainst all other voice.
Down, therefore, and beg mercy of the duke.

380   *Gra.* Beg that thou mayst have leave to hang thy-
      self ;
And yet, thy wealth being forfeit to the state,
Thou hast not left the value of a cord ;

---

374. *Contrive*, Plot.

Therefore thou must be hang'd at the state's charge.

Duke. That thou shalt see the difference of our spirits,
I pardon thee thy life before thou ask it :
For half thy wealth, it is Antonio's ;
The other half comes to the general state,
390 Which humbleness may drive unto a fine.

Por. Ay, for the state, not for Antonio.

Shy. [*in a hard toneless voice*]. Nay, take my life and all ; pardon not that :
You take my house when you do take the prop
That doth sustain my house ; you take my life
When you do take the means whereby I live.

Por. What mercy can you render him, Antonio ?

Gra. A halter gratis ; nothing else, for God's sake.

Ant. So please my lord the duke and all the court
400 To quit the fine for one half of his goods
I am content ; so he will let me have
The other half in use, to render it,
Upon his death, unto the gentleman
That lately stole his daughter :
Two things provided more, that, for this favour,
He presently become a Christian ;
The other, that he do record a gift,
Here in the court, of all he dies possess'd
Unto his son Lorenzo and his daughter.

410 *Duke.* He shall do this, or else I do recant
The pardon that I late pronouncèd here.

Por. Art thou contented, Jew? what dost thou say?

Shy. [*in the same toneless voice*]. I am content.

Por. Clerk, draw a deed of gift.

Shy. I pray you, give me leave to go from hence ;
I am not well : send the deed after me,
And I will sign it.

Duke. Get thee gone, but do it.

Gra. In christening shalt thou have two godfathers ;
420 Had I been judge, thou shouldst have had ten more,
To bring thee to the gallows, not the font.

[SHYLOCK *does not seem to hear the gibe. Slowly,
     as if half dazed, he goes from the court. The
     DUKE comes down from his dais to speak to
     PORTIA.*

Duke. Sir, I entreat you home with me to dinner.

Por. I humbly do desire your grace of pardon :
I must away this night to Padua,
And it is meet I presently set forth.

430 *Duke.* I am sorry that your leisure serves you not.
Antonio, gratify this gentleman,
For, in my mind, you are much bound to him.

[*Exit the* DUKE.

Bass. [*face to face with* PORTIA]. Most worthy gentle-
     man, I and my friend
Have by your wisdom been this day acquitted
Of grievous penalties ; in lieu whereof,
Three thousand ducats, due unto the Jew,
We freely cope your courteous pains withal.

440 *Ant.* And stand indebted, over and above,
In love and service to you evermore.

[PORTIA *looks whimsically down at* BASSANIO *as he
     bows over her hand, presenting her with the ducats.
     Her expression at once changes as he straightens
     himself, and she gives him back the money.*

Por. He is well paid that is well satisfied ;
And I, delivering you, am satisfied
And therein do account myself well paid :
[*To* BASSANIO] I pray you, know me when we meet
450   again :
I wish you well, and so I take my leave.

Bass. Dear sir, farewell.

[*They bow to one another, and she goes out with
     NERISSA. BASSANIO looks after her for a
     second, then turns to ANTONIO, and takes him
     by the hand.*

CURTAIN

431. *Gratify*, Thank and reward.   439. *Cope*, Requite, reward.

A LAMENTABLE COMEDY

(From *A Midsummer Night's Dream*)

PERSONS OF THE PLAY

THESEUS, *Duke of Athens.*
HIPPOLYTA, *Queen of the Amazons.*
PHILOSTRATE, *master of the revels to Theseus.*

PETER QUINCE, *a carpenter*		PROLOGUE.
NICK BOTTOM, *a weaver*	playing	PYRAMUS.
FRANCIS FLUTE, *a bellows-mender*	in the inter-	THISBE.
TOM SNOUT, *a tinker*	lude the	The WALL.
SNUG, *a joiner*	parts of	The LION.
ROBIN STARVELING, *a tailor*		MOONSHINE

OBERON, *king of the Fairies.*
TITANIA, *queen of the Fairies.*
PUCK, or ROBIN GOODFELLOW, *attendant on Oberon.*

PEASEBLOSSOM,
COBWEB,
MOTH, } *attendants on Titania.*
MUSTARDSEED,

A Fairy.
A Changeling Child.
Attendants on Theseus and Hippolyta, and other fairies
    in attendance on Oberon and Titania.

Situation.—Theseus, Duke of Athens, has married
Hippolyta, Queen of the Amazons, and, to entertain them
on the eve of their wedding, certain mechanics of Athens
prepare a play, a " lamentable comedy," as they call it.
The story of this play is that of the unhappy lovers Pyramus and Thisbe.   Their parents would not countenance

their marriage, and, conversing secretly through a hole in the wall which divided their houses, they arranged to meet outside their city at the tomb of Ninus below a white mulberry tree by a spring. Thisbe, coming first to the trysting-place, fled at the sight of a lioness stained with blood. She dropped her veil, which the fierce beast tore to pieces. Finding it rent and covered with blood, Pyramus thought his lady had been killed, and slew himself. Returning, she found him dead, and plunged his sword into her breast.

During the rehearsal of this play in a wood the chief actor is bewitched by the fairies, but the spell is lifted in time for the entertainment to take place.

Time occupied in acting the play: one hour and a quarter.

NOTE ON COSTUME

The play admits of many varieties of dress. The mechanics may appear as Elizabethan workmen, in doublet and hose, the doublets being made of coarse material resembling fustian, of russet or dark blue, perhaps enlivened by a well-placed patch, or they may wear Greek chitons, girdled and fastened on the shoulders with safety-pins, and sandals laced on with criss-cross thongs fastening just below the knee. Hippolyta should wear a long chiton of some soft material, with her hair dressed in the Greek fashion, and Theseus a chiton and a garland or diadem. Flaxman drawings or Greek sculpture should be consulted by the designer of classical dress, which admits of much variety, and, if properly draped, has a beautiful stage effect. If the stage is big, and the performance is given on a large scale, a procession of Greek warriors and Amazons bearing palm branches may be introduced at the opening of the last scene, for which Mendelssohn composed his famous wedding march.

The dress of the fairies may be in the old-fashioned ballet style, with the spread-out tarletan skirts, wand and wreath—a style which has much charm, though it is more elaborate and difficult to make than the clinging chiton which is usual in modern productions of fairy plays. Puck may be a faun-like little creature, with the pelt of some animal as a short tunic, and clusters of hazel-nuts or berried vine at his ears, or a brown elf in tight-fitting doublet and hose, and a peaked cap. Every one of the fairies should have some elfin quality. Much conventional representation of the fairy world entirely lacks this quality, which cannot be exactly described, though it is easily recognized.

SCENE I

A wood near Athens. At the back centre of the stage is a raised part, to serve as the bank where TITANIA *sleeps. Music of an odd and lively kind.*

[*Enter* PUCK, *dancing. His dance should be full of tricky and mischievous movements, and grotesque, almost uncouth gestures. He breaks off suddenly, curling up on* TITANIA'S *bank, holding up a branch before him, and peeping round it to eye the fairy. She enters to soft and dreamy music, and is, one would say, wafted across the stage, borne on the air like a star of thistledown or a puff of smoke, so lightly does she move. Her voice is sweet, clear, and rather vague, as if it came from the air.*]

Puck. How now, spirit ! whither wander you ?
Fai. Over hill, over dale,
> Thorough bush, thorough brier,
Over park, over pale,
> Thorough flood, thorough fire,
I do wander everywhere,
Swifter than the moonës sphere ;
And I serve the fairy queen,
To dew her orbs upon the green.
The cowslips tall her pensioners be :
In their gold coats spots you see ;
Those be rubies, fairy favours,
In those freckles live their savours ;

l must go seek some dewdrops here
And hang a pearl in every cowslip's ear.
30 Farewell, thou lob of spirits ; I'll be gone :
Our queen and all her elves come here anon.
    Puck [pointing at her warningly with his branch].
        The king doth keep his revels here to-night :
Take heed the queen come not within his sight ;
For Oberon is passing fell and wrath,
Because that she as her attendant hath
A lovely boy, stolen from an Indian king ;
She never had so sweet a changeling ;
And jealous Oberon would have the child
40 Knight of his train, to trace the forests wild—
But make room, fairy ! here comes Oberon.
    Fai. And here my mistress. Would that he were
      gone !

[*Enter from the left* OBERON, *swiftly and lightly. He
    stands poised by* PUCK, *who squats like a little frog
    at his feet. Enter from the right* TITANIA'S *four
    fairies,* MUSTARDSEED *strutting,* COBWEB *with a
    soft waving movement,* PEASEBLOSSOM *dancing a
    gay little fluttering step,* MOTH *as if she were flying.*
50   *All pause with tiny shrill cries as they see* OBERON.
    They are followed by the* QUEEN, *who holds her
    changeling by the hand. She stands still and
    straight, looking at* OBERON.

    Obe. Ill met by moonlight, proud Titania.
    Tita. What, jealous Oberon ! Fairies, skip hence :
I have forsworn his bed and company.
               [*The Fairies whisk into corners.*
    Obe. Why should Titania cross her Oberon ?
I do but beg a little changeling boy,
60 To be my henchman.
    Tita. [putting her arm round the boy]. Set your heart
      at rest :

      35. *Fell*, Fierce.   60. *Henchman*, Page.

The fairy land buys not the child of me.

Obe. How long within this wood intend you
    stay?

Tita. Perchance till after Theseus' wedding-day.
If you will patiently dance in our round
And see our moonlight revels, go with us;
If not, shun me, and I will spare your haunts.

70 *Obe.* Give me that boy, and I will go with thee.

Tita. Not for thy fairy kingdom. Fairies, away!
We shall chide downright, if I longer stay.

> [*She goes out in a very queenly way, with her
> attendants.*

Obe. [*very much the king and master*]. Well, go thy
    way: thou shalt not from this grove
Till I torment thee for this injury.

[*To* PUCK, *who leaps up and stands ready*] Fetch me
    that flower, that herb I showed thee once,

80 The juice of it on sleeping eyelids laid
Will make or man or woman madly dote
Upon the next live creature that it sees.
And maidens call it love-in-idleness.
Fetch me this herb; and be thou here again
Ere the leviathan can swim a league.

Puck. I'll put a girdle round about the earth
In forty minutes.

> [*He spins off, arms out, head a little bent.* OBERON
> *stands aside, holding fern fronds before him.*
> 90 *Enter Titania's Fairies. They dart about as if
> searching for a sign of the enemy, but they do not
> see* OBERON. *They go off with little sighs of
> relief, and bring in* TITANIA *to soft light music.*

Tita.   Sing me now asleep;
Then to your offices and let me rest.

> [*She lies on her bank, and the* Fairies *dance a
> slumber dance, and sing a slumber song, helped
> by singers behind the scenes.*

---

85. *Leviathan*, Huge sea-monster.

Fir. F. You spotted snakes with double tongue,
100   Thorny hedgehogs, be not seen ;
     Newts and blind-worms, do no wrong,
        Come not near our fairy queen,
Chorus.—Philomel, with melody,
        Sing in our sweet lullaby :
     Lulla, lulla, lullaby, lulla, lulla, lullaby :
        Never harm
        Nor spell nor charm,
     Come our lovely lady nigh ;
     So, good-night, with lullaby.
110   *Fir. F.* Weaving spiders, come not here ;
        Hence, you long-legg'd spinners, hence !
     Beetles black, approach not near ;
        Worm nor snail, do no offence.
Chorus.—Philomel, with melody, etc.
Fir. F. Hence, away ! now all is well :
     One aloof, stand sentinel.

[*The* Fairies *creep away to music which grows
fainter, and the changeling is left to guard*
120   Titania. Oberon *steps forward and touches
him with his fern fronds, and he rolls over,
fast asleep.* Puck *creeps in with the flower,
and gives it to* Oberon, *who presses its juice
on to the eyelids of* Titania, *and in a low
mysterious voice speaks the spell.*

Obe. What thou seest when thou dost wake,
     Do it for thy true-love take,
     Love and languish for his sake :
     Be it ounce, or cat, or bear,

---

103. *Philomel.* King Tereus, tiring of his wife Procne, cut out her
tongue, and, pretending she was dead, took her sister Philomela as his wife. But Procne wove the story of her wrongs
into a web of tapestry, which she sent to Philomela. The
vengeance of the sisters was a terrible one, and the gods, in
anger, transformed Tereus into a cruel hawk, Procne into a
swallow, ever restless, and Philomela into a nightingale,
remembering the pain of her story in her wild sad song.

128. *Ounce.* A wild animal somewhat resembling the *pard*, or
leopard.

130

Pard, or boar with bristled hair,
In thy eye that shall appear
When thou wak'st, it is thy dear:
Wake when some vile thing is near.

[*He steals away, followed by* PUCK. *After a moment's pause, enter* PETER QUINCE, *carrying a roll of paper. His demeanour is that of a rather simple fellow delighted to find himself at the head of a great enterprise, and full of secretive importance. Then in comes* NICK BOTTOM, *brimming with self-satisfaction;* SNUG, *very conscientious and very slow-witted;* SNOUT, *a phlegmatic individual who betrays no sign of his feelings;* STARVELING, *who looks as if his private opinion is that the enterprise on which they are engaged may quite likely turn out to be a failure; and* FLUTE, *a youth with wispy hair and a girlish complexion, whose voice has just broken and is unreliable as such a voice can be. In their various ways they brace themselves for the ordeal of the rehearsal which is about to take place.*

Bot. [*with the air of a sleuth*]. Are we all met ?

Quince. Pat, pat ; and here's a marvellous convenient place for our rehearsal of [*consulting his roll and reading slowly*] The-most-lamentable-comedy-and-most-cruel-death-of-Pyramus-and-Thisby. This green plot shall be our stage, this hawthorn-brake our tiring-house ; and we will do it in action as we will do it before the Duke.

[*Signs of excitement and consternation among the actors.*

Bot. [*with the air of a man who has something really important to say*]. Peter Quince——

Quince. What sayest thou, bully Bottom ?

---

152. *Pat*, Just at the right moment.
157. *Tiring-house*, Actors' attiring-room.
163. *Bully*, Fine fellow, used as a term of endearment.

Bot. [*scandalized*]. There are things in this comedy of Pyramus and Thisby that will never please. First, Pyramus must draw a sword to kill himself ; which the ladies cannot abide. How answer you that ?

Snout. By'r lakin, a parlous fear.

Star. I believe we must leave the killing out, when 170 all is done.

Bot. [*with the air of a man who has a solution ready for every problem*]. Not a whit : I have a device to make all well. Write me a prologue ; and let the prologue seem to say, we will do no harm with our swords, and that Pyramus is not killed indeed ; and, for the more better assurance, tell them that I Pyramus am not Pyramus, but Bottom the weaver : this will put them out of fear.   [*General approval.*

Quince. Well, we will have such a prologue ; and it 180 shall be written in eight and six.

Bot. No, make it two more ; let it be written in eight and eight.

Snout. Will not the ladies be afeard of the lion ?

Star. I fear it, I promise you.

Bot. [*aghast at the very idea*]. Masters, you ought to consider with yourselves ; to bring in—God shield us ! —a lion among ladies, is a most dreadful thing ; for there is not a more fearful wild-fowl than your lion living ; and we ought to look to't.

190 *Snout.* Therefore another prologue must tell he is not a lion.

Bot. [*waving aside a suggestion which is not his own*]. Nay, you must name his name, and half his face must be seen through the lion's neck : and he himself must speak through, saying thus, or to the same defect [*clears his throat, and assumes the attitude of the orator*], " Ladies,"—or " Fair ladies,—I would wish you,"—or

168. *By'r lakin*, By our ladykin, a mild oath ; like " marry," by (the Virgin) Mary.
168. *Parlous*, Perilous, dreadful.
180. *Eight and six*, The favourite measure of the old popular ballads.

" I would request you,"—or " I would entreat you,"
—not to fear, not to tremble : my life for yours. If
200 you think I come hither as a lion, it were pity of my
life : no, I am no such thing ; I am a man as other
men are ; " [*Suddenly dropping the rhetorical manner*]
and there, indeed, let him name his name, and tell
them plainly he is Snug the joiner.

Quince [*looking rather doubtfully at* SNUG, *who
scratches his head, evidently feeling that this effort will
be beyond his powers*]. Well, it shall be so. But there
is two hard things ; that is, to bring the moonlight
into a chamber ; for, you know, Pyramus and Thisby
210 meet by moonlight.

Snout. Doth the moon shine that night we play our
play ?

Bot. A calendar, a calendar ! look in the almanac,
find out moonshine, find out moonshine.

[*A prolonged consultation of an almanac produced
by* QUINCE.

Quince [*rubbing his hands*]. Yes, it doth shine that
night.

Bot. Why, then you may leave a casement of the
220 great chamber window, where we play, open, and the
moon may shine in at the casement.

Quince. Ay ; or else one must come in with a bush
of thorns and a lanthorn, and say he comes to disfigure,
or to present, the person of Moonshine. Then, there
is another thing : we must have a wall in the great
chamber ; for Pyramus and Thisby, says the story,
did talk through the chink of a wall.

[*All the actors look staggered at the thought of this
difficulty.*

230 *Snug.* You can never bring in a wall. What say you,
Bottom ?

Bot. [*with the gesture of one who has seen a way out*].
Some man or other must present Wall : and let him
have some plaster, or some loam, or some rough-cast
about him, to signify wall ; and let him hold his fingers

thus, and through that cranny shall Pyramus and
Thisby whisper.

Quince. If that may be, then all is well. Come, sit
down, every mother's son, and rehearse your parts.
240 Pyramus, you begin : when you have spoken your
speech, enter into that brake : and so every one
according to his cue.

[PUCK *creeps in.*]

Puck [*shrinking to one side of the stage, finger on lip*].
What hempen homespuns have we swaggering
here,
So near the cradle of the fairy queen ?
What, a play toward ! I'll be an auditor ;
An actor too perhaps, if I see cause.
250   *Quince.* Speak, Pyramus. Thisby, stand forth.
[*The hero and heroine stand at some distance from
one another, both facing the audience, as if say-
ing a recitation.* THISBY *nervously plucks at
his doublet ;* PYRAMUS *is prepared to show all
hearers what good acting is.*
Pyramus [*in a loud and yet sentimental tone*]. Thisby,
the flower of odious savours sweet——
Quince [*scandalized, prompting*]. Odours, odours.
Bot.   ——Odours savours sweet :
260 So hath thy breath, my dearest Thisby dear.
But hark ! a voice ! stay thou but here awhile,
And by-and-by I will to thee appear.   [*Struts off.*
Puck. A stranger Pyramus than e'er played here.
[*Slips after him.*
Flute [*as* THISBY, *in a paroxysm of stage fright*].
Must I speak now ?
Quince. Ay, marry, must you ; for you must under-
stand he goes but to see a noise that he heard, and is
to come again.
270   [*For a few seconds* FLUTE *blinks and fidgets, then,
with startling suddenness, he bursts forth——*
Most radiant Pyramus, most lily-white of hue,

Of colour like the red rose on triumphant [*swallows*]
    brier,
Most brisky juvenal and eke most lovely Jew,
As true as truest horse [*moistens his lips*] that yet
    would never tire.
[*His voice suddenly high-pitched*] I'll meet thee,
    Pyramus, at Ninny's tomb.

280   *Quince* [*superbly patient*]. "Ninus' tomb," man:
why, you must not speak that yet ; that you answer
to Pyramus : you speak all your part at once, cues
and all. Pyramus, enter : your cue is past ; it is,
"never tire."

    This. O,—as true as truest horse, that yet would
never tire.

[*Enter* Bottom, *with an ass's head.* Puck *follows him,
    slinking secretly along like a small boy who has just
    brought off a piece of mischief.*]

290   *Pyramus* [*in an intensely sentimental voice*]. If I
were fair, Thisby, I were only thine.
    Quince [*beside himself*]. O monstrous ! O strange !
we are haunted. Pray, masters ! fly, masters ! Help !
    [*They rush out helter-skelter, followed by* Puck, *in
        highest delight.* Bottom *stands gazing after
        them.*
    Bot. Why do they run away ? this is a knavery of
them to make me afeard.

[Snout *steals in.*]

300   *Snout*. O Bottom, thou art changed ! what do I see
on thee ?
    Bot. What do you see ? You see an ass-head of
your own, do you ?
    [*He makes a movement towards* Snout, *who de-
    parts in a hurry.*

275. *Juvenal,* Young man.

[QUINCE *adventures in, and comes up to* BOTTOM.]

Quince. Bless thee, Bottom ! bless thee ! thou art translated.   [*Exit in sudden panic.*

Bot. I see their knavery ! this is to make an ass of
310 me, to fright me, if they could.   But I will not stir from this place, do what they can : I will walk up and down here, and I will sing, that they shall hear I am not afraid.

[*Sings in a hoarse tuneless voice*]—

> The ousel cock so black of hue,
>   With orange-tawny bill,
> The throstle with his note so true,
>   The wren with little quill——

Tita. [*in a drowsy enchanted voice, half rising from
320 her couch*]. What angel wakes me from my flowery bed ?

Bot. [*singing on*]—

> The finch, the sparrow and the lark,
>   The plain-song cuckoo gray,
> Whose note full many a man doth mark,
>   And dares not answer nay ;——

[*With dignity*] for, indeed, who would set his wit to so foolish a bird ? who would give a bird the lie, though he cry " cuckoo " never so ?

[TITANIA *rises from her bed, and steals across the
330   stage until she stands face to face with* BOTTOM.
          *She speaks to him as if enchanted with his
          beauty and the harmony of his song.*

Tita. I pray thee, gentle mortal, sing again :
Mine ear is much enamour'd of thy note ;
So is mine eye enthralled to thy shape ;
And thy fair virtue's force perforce doth move me
On the first view to say, to swear, I love thee.

Bot. [*with all politeness*]. Methinks, mistress, you should have little reason for that : and yet, to say the
340 truth, reason and love keep little company together

---

323. *Plain-song*, Simple chant, as compared with the elaborate prick-song, which has many variations.

nowadays ; the more the pity that some honest neighbours will not make them friends. [*Preening himself*] Nay, I can gleek upon occasion.

Tita. [*adoring him*]. Thou art as wise as thou art beautiful.

Bot. [*with a little bow*]. Not so, neither : but if I had wit enough to get out of this wood, I have enough to serve mine own turn.

Tita. [*clasping her arms round one of his*]. Out of
350   this wood do not desire to go :
Thou shalt remain here, whether thou wilt or no.
I am a spirit of no common rate :
The summer still doth tend upon my state ;
And I do love thee : therefore, go with me :
I'll give thee fairies to attend on thee,
And they shall fetch thee jewels from the deep,
And sing while thou on pressèd flowers dost sleep :
And I will purge thy mortal grossness so
That thou shalt like an airy spirit go.
360 Peaseblossom ! Cobweb ! Moth ! and Mustardseed !
          [*Each* Fairy *comes at the call of his name.*

Peas. Ready.
Cob.   And I.
Moth.   And I.
Mus.   And I.
All.   Where shall we go ?
Tita. Be kind and courteous to this gentleman :
Come, wait upon him ; lead him to my bower,
Tie up my love's tongue, bring him silently.
370   [*The* Fairies *cast garlands of flowers round him, and
          with tiny strutting steps, as if walking in an
          elfin procession, lead him away, while* TITANIA,
          hands clasped, watches his heavy shambling gait
          in ecstasy.*

CURTAIN

343. *Gleek,* Speak satirically.

SCENE II

TITANIA'S *bower*.

[TITANIA *enters, leading* BOTTOM, *who wears a wreath of roses, slightly to one side. The four* Fairies *are in attendance. In one corner of the stage* OBERON *stands watching, holding up a fern frond before him*.]

Tita. Come, sit thee down upon this flowery bed,
While I thy amiable cheeks do coy,
10 And stick musk-roses in thy sleek, smooth head,
And kiss thy fair large ears, my gentle joy.
[*She twines her arms round him, petting him*.
Bot. [*with slight impatience*]. Where's Peaseblossom?
Peas. Ready.
Bot. Scratch my head, Peaseblossom. [*Heaves a sigh of relief as the* Fairy *obeys*.] Where's Mounsieur Cobweb?
Cob. Ready.
Bot. [*with great politeness*]. Mounsieur Cobweb, good
20 mounsieur, get you your weapons in your hand, and kill me a red-hipped humble-bee on the top of a thistle ; and, good mounsieur, bring me the honey-bag. Do not fret yourself too much in the action, mounsieur ; and, good mounsieur, have a care the honey-bag break not ; I would be loth to have you overflown with a honey-bag, signior. Where's Mounsieur Mustardseed?
Mus. Ready.
Bot. Give me your neaf, Mounsieur Mustardseed.
30 [MUSTARDSEED *obeys, with a splendid bow*.] Pray you, leave your courtesy, good mounsieur.
Mus. What's your will?

9. *Coy*, Fondle.   29. *Neaf*, Fist.

Bot. Nothing, good mounsieur, but to help Cavalery
Cobweb to scratch. I must to the barber's, mounsieur ; for methinks I am marvellous hairy about the
face ; and I am such a tender ass, if my hair do but
tickle me, I must scratch.

Tita. What, wilt thou hear some music, my sweet
love ?

40 *Bot.* I have a reasonable good ear in music. Let's
have the tongs and the bones. [*Rough music.*

Tita. Or say, sweet love, what thou desir'st to eat.

Bot. Truly, a peck of provender ; I could much
your good dry oats. Methinks I have a great desire to
a bottle of hay ; good hay, sweet hay, hath no fellow.

Tita. I have a venturous fairy that shall seek
The squirrel's hoard, and fetch thee thence new nuts.

Bot. I had rather have a handful or two of dried
peas. But, I pray you, let none of your people stir
50 me : I have an exposition of sleep come upon me.

Tita. Sleep thou, and I will wind thee in my arms.
Fairies, be gone, and be all ways away.

[*The* Fairies *creep out.*

So doth the woodbine the sweet honeysuckle
Gently entwist ; the female ivy so
Enrings the barky fingers of the elm.
O, how I love thee ! how I dote on thee ! [*They sleep.*

[OBERON *comes forward and regards them.*

[*Enter* PUCK, *and hugs himself with delight at the
60 success of the spell.*]

Obe. Welcome, good Robin. See'st thou this sweet
sight ?
Her dotage now I do begin to pity :
For, meeting her of late behind the wood,
Seeking sweet favours for this hateful fool,
I did upbraid her, and fall out with her,

41. *Tongs,* Played on with a key to produce " music."
45. *Bottle,* Bundle.
54. *Woodbine.* Here, the bindweed, or great convolvulus.

And she in mild terms begg'd my patience.
I then did ask of her her changeling child ;
Which straight she gave me, and her fairy sent
70 To bear him to my bower in fairy land.
And now I have the boy, I will undo
This hateful imperfection of her eyes :
And, gentle Puck, take this transformed scalp
From off the head of this Athenian swain.
But first I will release the fairy queen.

> [*He touches her eyelids with a white flower.*
>
> Be as thou wast wont to be ;
> See as thou wast wont to see :
> Dian's bud o'er Cupid's flower
> 80   Hath such force and blessed power.

Now, my Titania ; wake you, my sweet queen.

Tita. [*drowsily and fearfully*]. My Oberon, what
visions have I seen !
Methought I was enamoured of an ass.

Obe. There lies your love.

Tita. [*shrinking away from him in horror*]. How
came these things to pass ?
O, how mine eyes do loathe his visage now !

Obe. Sound music !   Come, my queen, take hands
90   with me.

> [*Soft light music.* OBERON *and* TITANIA *dance
> out, with a gentle, drifting movement.*

Puck [*taking the ass's head from* BOTTOM]. Now,
when thou wak'st, with thine own fool's eyes
peep.

> [*He runs out.* BOTTOM *awakes, in the uneasy way
> of a man who has slept in his clothes and in
> a rather uncomfortable position. He fidgets,
> snores, grunts, and yawns.*

100   *Bot.* [*half asleep*]. When my cue comes, call me, and
I will answer : my next is " most fair Pyramus."
[*With a great yawn*] Heigh-ho ! [*Sitting up and looking about him*] Peter Quince !   Flute, the bellows-
mender !   Snout, the tinker !   God's my life, stolen

hence, and left me asleep! [*Blinks.*] I have had a most
rare vision. [*Blinks, with a beatific smile.*] I have had
a dream, past the wit of man to say what dream it was :
man is but an ass, if he go about to expound this
dream.   Methought I was [*begins to look doubtful and
110 rather alarmed*]—there is no man can tell what.   Methought I was [*feels his chin, with increasing doubt*]—
and methought I had [*feels the top of his head, and his
ears, and is evidently surprised and relieved to find them
the size of the normal human ear*]—but man is but a
patched fool, if he will offer to say *what* methought I
had.   [*Declaiming*] The eye of man hath not heard,
the ear of man hath not seen, man's hand is not able
to taste, his tongue to conceive, nor his heart to report, what my dream was.
120   [*Sits for a moment, hands on knees, in rumina-
        tion, shakes his head, gets up slowly, and goes
        heavily out.*

. **CURTAIN**

SCENE III

A hall in the palace of THESEUS. THESEUS *and*
HIPPOLYTA *may enter in procession with warriors and
Amazons, or may be seated on a dais when the curtain
goes up, with* PHILOSTRATE *in attendance.*

The. Come now ; what masques, what dances shall
        we have ?
What revels are in hand ?   How shall we beguile
The lazy time, if not with some delight ?
10   *Phil.* [*giving him a paper*]. There is a brief how
        many sports are ripe :
Make choice of which your highness will see first.

10. *Brief,* A short statement.

The. [*reading*]. " A tedious brief scene of young
     Pyramus
And his love Thisby ; very tragical mirth."
Merry and tragical ! tedious and brief !
That is, hot ice and wondrous strange snow.
What are they that do play it ?
Phil. Hard-handed men that work in Athens here,
20 Which never laboured in their minds till now,
And now have toiled their unbreathed memories
With this same play, against your nuptial.
The. I will hear that play ;
For never anything can be amiss,
When simpleness and duty tender it.
Go, bring them in.   [*Exit* PHILOSTRATE.
Hip. I love not to see wretchedness o'ercharged
And duty in his service perishing.
The. Why, gentle sweet, you shall see no such thing.
30 *Hip.* He says they can do nothing in this kind.
The. The kinder we, to give them thanks for noth-
          ing.
Our sport shall be to take what they mistake :
And what poor duty would, but cannot do,
Noble respect takes it in might, not merit.

          [*Re-enter* PHILOSTRATE.]

Phil. So please your grace, the Prologue is ad-
          dressed.
The. Let him approach.

40 [*Flourish of trumpets. Enter* QUINCE, *in a flowing
     robe, crowned with a garland, and holding a roll of
     paper. He is almost petrified with nervousness,
     but fixes a glassy eye on some point in space and
     speaks out well.*]

Pro. If we offend, it is with our good will.
That you should think, we come not to offend,

_____

21. *Unbreathed*, Unexercised.   37. *Addressed*, Made ready.

But with good will.   To show our simple skill,
That is the true beginning of our end.
Consider, then, we come but in despite.
50 We do not come as minding to content you,
Our true intent is.   All for your delight
We are not here.   That you should here repent you,
The actors are at hand, and by their show
You shall know all that you are like to know.

> [*He swallows hard, mops his brow, and beckons to
> the actors waiting for their cue.*

The. This fellow doth not stand upon points.

Hip. He hath rid his prologue like a rough colt ;
he knows not the stop.   A good moral, my lord : it is
60 not enough to speak, but to speak true.

The. Who is next ?

> [*A march played with comic emphasis.   Enter* PYRA-
> MUS *and* THISBY, WALL, MOONSHINE, *and* LION.
> WALL *wears boards slung across his shoulders like
> those of a sandwich-man, and painted to represent
> red brick walls ;* MOONSHINE *has a lantern, a
> bundle of thorns, and a toy dog on a string ;* LION
> *has a lion's skin, with his own face appearing below
> the head of the beast.   Every actor is suffering a
> 70 little from stage fright, with the exception of* PYRA-
> MUS, *whose importance and pleasure know no
> bounds.   They stand in a row, and* QUINCE *presents
> them to* THESEUS *and the audience.*]

Pro. Gentles, perchance you wonder at this show ;
But wonder on, till truth make all things plain !
This man is Pyramus, if you would know ;

> [PYRAMUS *smirks and bows.*

This beauteous lady Thisby is certain.

> [THISBY *gives a sort of scared curtsy.*

80 This man, with lime and rough-cast, doth present

---

57. *Stand upon points*. In two senses—mind his stops, and trouble
about small politenesses of behaviour.

Wall, that vile Wall which did these lovers sunder ;
And through Wall's chink, poor souls, they are con-
      tent
To whisper.   At the which let no man wonder.
                              [WALL *stiffly inclines his head.*
This man with lantern, dog, and bush of thorn,
Presenteth Moonshine ; for, if you will know,
By Moonshine did these lovers think no scorn
To meet at Ninus' tomb, there, there to woo.
90   [MOONSHINE *blinks, and forgets to make his*
                  obeisance.
This grisly beast, which Lion hight by name,
                              [LION *touches his forelock.*
The trusty Thisby, coming first by night,
Did scare away, or rather did affright ;
And, as she fled, her mantle she did fall,
Which Lion vile with bloody mouth did stain.
Anon comes Pyramus, sweet youth and tall,
And finds his trusty Thisby's mantle slain :
100 Whereat, with blade, with bloody blameful blade,
He bravely broach'd his boiling bloody breast ;
And Thisby, tarrying in mulberry shade,
His dagger drew, and died.   For all the rest,
Let Lion, Moonshine, Wall, and Lovers twain
At large discourse, while here they do remain.
      [*Exeunt* PROLOGUE, PYRAMUS, THISBY, LION, *and*
      MOONSHINE.
  Wall [*advancing and speaking his piece without the
      slightest change of expression in face or voice*].
110   In this same interlude it doth befall
That I, one Snout by name, present a wall ;
And such a wall, as I would have you think,
That had in it a crannied hole or chink,
Through which the lovers, Pyramus and Thisby,
Did whisper often very secretly.
This loam, this rough-cast, and this stone doth show

------

91. *Hight*, Is called.

That I am that same wall, the truth is so :
And this the cranny is, right and sinister,
Through which the fearful lovers are to whisper.

120 [*Enter* PYRAMUS, *with the gesture and gait he believes*
appropriate to the tragic hero.]

Pyr. O grim-look'd night ! O night with hue so
black !
O night, which ever art when day is not !
O night, O night, alack, alack, alack,
I fear my Thisby's promise is forgot !
And thou, O wall, O sweet, O lovely wall,
That stand'st between her father's ground and mine !
Thou wall, O wall, O sweet and lovely wall,
130 Show me thy chink, to blink through with mine eyne !
[WALL *holds up his fingers.*
Thanks, courteous wall : Jove shield thee well for this !
[*Looks through the chink.*
But what see I ? No Thisby do I see.
O wicked wall, through whom I see no bliss !
Cursed be thy stones for thus deceiving me !
The. The wall, methinks, being sensible, should
curse again.
Pyr. [*kindly explaining*]. No, in truth, sir, he should
140 not. "Deceiving me" is Thisby's cue : she is to
enter now, and I am to spy her through the wall. You
shall see, it will fall pat as I told you. Yonder she
comes.

[*Re-enter* THISBY.]

This. O wall, full often hast thou heard my moans,
For parting my fair Pyramus and me !
My cherry lips have often kiss'd thy stones,
Thy stones with lime and hair knit up in thee.
Pyr. I see a voice : now will I to the chink,
150 To spy an I can hear my Thisby's face.
Thisby !

118. *Sinister*, Left.

This. My love ! thou art my love, I think.

Pyr. Think what thou wilt, I am thy lover's grace,
And, like Limander, am I trusty still.

This. And I, like Helen, till the Fates me kill.

Pyr. Not Shafalus to Procrus was so true.

This. As Shafalus to Procrus, I to you.

Pyr. O, kiss me through the hole of this vile wall !

This. [*after a prolonged effort*]. I kiss the wall's hole,
160   not your lips at all.

Pyr. Wilt thou at Ninny's tomb meet me straight-
way ?

This. 'Tide life, 'tide death, I come without delay.

            [*Exeunt* PYRAMUS *and* THISBY.

Wall. Thus have I, Wall, my part discharged so ;
And, being done, thus Wall away doth go.

                [*Goes off stolidly.*

Hip. This is the silliest stuff that ever I heard.

The. The best in this kind are but shadows ; and the
170 worst are no worse, if imagination amend them.

Hip. It must be your imagination then, and not
theirs.

The. If we imagine no worse of them than they of
themselves, they may pass as excellent men. Here
come two noble beasts in, a man and a lion.

      [*Re-enter* LION *and* MOONSHINE.]

Lion. You, ladies, you, whose gentle hearts do fear
The smallest monstrous mouse that creeps on floor,
May now perchance both quake and tremble here,
180 When lion rough in wildest rage doth roar.
Then know that I, one Snug the joiner, am
A lion fell, nor else no lion's dam ;
For, if I should as lion come in strife
Into this place, 'twere pity on my life.

---

154. *Limander.* For Leander, who swam the Hellespont every night
     to visit his lady, Hero.

156. *Shafalus.* For Cephalus, who, indifferent to the love of the
     dawn-goddess Aurora, cared only for the maiden Procris.

The. A very gentle beast, and of a good conscience.

Hip. Let us listen to the Moon.

Moon. [*raising it*]. This lanthorn doth the hornèd
    moon present ;
Myself the man i' the moon do seem to be.

190   *The.* This is the greatest error of all the rest : the
man should be put into the lanthorn. How is it else
the man i' the moon ?

Hip. I am aweary of this moon ; would he would
change !

The. It appears, by his small light of discretion,
that he is in the wane ; but yet, in courtesy, in all
reason, we must stay the time.

Hip. Proceed, Moon.

Moon. [*rather crossly*]. All that I have to say is, to
200 tell you that the lanthorn is the moon ; I, the man
in the moon ; this thorn-bush, my thorn-bush ; and
this dog, my dog.

The. Why, all these should be in the lanthorn ; for
all these are in the moon. But, silence ! here comes
Thisby.

[*Re-enter* THISBY.]

This. This is old Ninny's tomb. Where is my love ?

Lion [*roaring*]. Oh——   [THISBY *hurries away.*

The. Well roared, Lion.

210   *Hip.* Well run, Thisby. Well shone, Moon. Truly,
the moon shines with a good grace.

[*The* LION *shakes* THISBY'S *mantle, and exit.*

The. Well moused, Lion.

Hip. And so the lion vanished.

The. And then came Pyramus.

[*Re-enter* PYRAMUS.]

Pyr. Sweet Moon, I thank thee for thy sunny beams :
I thank thee, Moon, for shining now so bright ;
For, by thy gracious, golden, glittering gleams,

220 I trust to take of truest Thisby sight.

[Sees torn mantle.

But stay, O spite !
But mark, poor knight,
What dreadful dole is here !
Eyes, do you see ?
How can it be ?
O dainty duck ! O dear !
Thy mantle good,
What, stain'd with blood !

230 Approach, ye Furies fell !
O Fates, come, come,
Cut thread and thrum ;
Quail, crush, conclude, and quell !

The. This passion, and the death of a dear friend, would go near to make a man look sad.

Hip. Beshrew my heart, but I pity the man.

Pyr. [*with renewed passion*]. O, wherefore, Nature, didst thou lions frame ?

Since lion vile hath here deflower'd my dear :
240 Which is—no, no—which was the fairest dame
That lived, that loved, that liked, that look'd with cheer.

Come tears, confound ;
Out, sword, and wound
The pap of Pyramus ;
Ay, that left pap,
Where heart doth hop :   *[Stabs himself.*
Thus die I, thus, thus, thus.

[Sinks carefully to the ground.

250 Now am I dead,
Now am I fled ;

230. *Furies*, Snaky-haired divinities of the under-world, who tormented evildoers with the stings and lashings of remorse.
231. *Fates.* The three grey sisters, one of whom span the thread of human destiny, one wove it into fabric, and one cut it off when death should come to a man.
232. *Thrum*, The end of the weaver's thread, left after tying.
233. *Quell*, Kill.

My soul is in the sky ;
Tongue, lose thy light ;
Moon, take thy flight :

[Exit MOONSHINE.

Now die, die, die, die, die.

The. Here comes Thisby.

Hip. She hath spied him already with those sweet eyes.

260   *This.* Asleep, my love ?
What, dead, my dove ?
O, Pyramus, arise !
Speak, speak. Quite dumb ?
Dead, dead ? A tomb
Must cover thy sweet eyes.

       [Kneeling and gazing at him in woe.

These lily lips,
This cherry nose,
These yellow cowslip cheeks,
270   Are gone, are gone :
Lovers, make moan :
His eyes were green as leeks.
O Sisters Three,
Come, come to me,
With hands as pale as milk :
Lay them in gore,
Since you have shore
With shears his thread of silk.
Tongue, not a word :
280   Come, trusty sword ;
Come, blade, my breast imbrue :

       [Stabs herself.

And farewell, friends ;
Thus Thisby ends :
Adieu, adieu, adieu.   *[Dies.*

The. Moonshine and Lion are left to bury the dead.

---

284. *Thus Thisby ends.* An allusion in a seventeenth-century play shows that the old " business " was for Thisby to stab herself with the scabbard of the sword.

Hip. Ay, and Wall too.

Bot. [*starting up*]. No, I assure you; the wall is down that parted their fathers. Will it please you to
290 see the epilogue, or to hear a Bergomask dance between two of our company?

The. Come, your Bergomask: let your epilogue alone.

　　　[*A roisterous country dance, at the end of which the
　　　clock strikes twelve.*

CURTAIN

290. *Bergomask dance,* A rustic dance, such as those of the peasants of Bergamo, a province in the state of Venice.

THE MASQUE FOR MIRANDA

(From *The Tempest*)

PERSONS OF THE MASQUE

PROSPERO, *an enchanter, dwelling on an enchanted island.*
MIRANDA, *his daughter.*
FERDINAND, *prince of Naples, who, wrecked on the island,
    has fallen in love with Miranda.*
ARIEL, *an airy spirit, who serves Prospero.*
IRIS,
CERES,
JUNO,   } *presented by Spirits, who play the masque*
Nymphs,
Reapers,

The time occupied in presenting this masque depends
on the length of the dances introduced—it will probably
be twenty minutes to half an hour.

NOTE ON COSTUME

Prospero should wear an enchanter's robe of scarlet or
flame colour ornamented with cabbalistic signs in stencil
or appliqué. Miranda's dress is made with hanging
sleeves and a girdle, and she is crowned with a wreath
of tiny flowers. Ferdinand wears tunic and hose, and
a cap with a feather. Ariel and the goddesses may be
habited in the classical chiton, Ariel's garment being
made of flimsy material, and jagged at the edges, to look
as loose and floating and cloud-like as possible. The
dress of the figure of Puck in Blake's drawing in the

National Gallery of the Midsummer Night's Dream
fairies dancing is a good model for a stage Ariel.   Particular care is needed in casting the parts for a successful
representation of this masque—Prospero must have a
beautiful voice, Ferdinand and Miranda must seem the
very incarnation of the spirit of youth, the goddesses
must suggest their qualities in their movement and
appearance, and Ariel—one of the conceptions of Shakespeare's mind hardly ever satisfactorily shown on the
stage—should be able to trick the audience into believing
that he is indeed a " gay creature of the element." With
regard to the dancers, the " sunburnt sicklemen " may
wear smocks and rye-straw hats ; the nymphs gay and
simple dresses of bright colour.   The orthodox peasant's
dress has become dulled with too much usage, and it is
generally a mistake to cover the head and neck of a
dancer with the cotton sun-bonnet that often appears in
old English dances.   A garland, or side knots of flowers,
should be worn in preference to this.

SCENE

Near the cave of PROSPERO *the enchanter.   His
daughter* MIRANDA *and her lover* FERDINAND *stand
before him.*

Pros. [*joining their hands*]. O Ferdinand, I
Have given you here a thrid of mine own life,
Or that for which I live : here, afore Heaven,
I ratify this my rich gift.   O Ferdinand,
Do not smile at me that I boast her off,
10 For thou shalt find she will outstrip all praise
And make it halt behind her.
Fer.   I do believe it
Against an oracle.
Pros.   Fairly spoke.
Sit then and talk with her ; she is thine own.

6. *Thrid*, Thread.

[FERDINAND *leads* MIRANDA *to a mossy bank right
of the stage, and they sit there together.*
What, Ariel ! my industrious servant, Ariel !

[*Music. Enter* ARIEL. *He may come swiftly or slowly,
but it must be with ethereal lightness and perfect
harmony of movement.*

   Ari. All hail, great master ! grave sir, hail ! I come
To answer thy best pleasure ; be't to fly,
To swim, to dive into the fire, to ride
On the curl'd clouds, to thy strong bidding task
Ariel and all his quality.
   Pros.   Go bring the spirits,
O'er whom I give thee power, here to this place :
Incite them to quick motion ; for I must
Bestow upon the eyes of this young couple
Some vanity of mine art : it is my promise,
And they expect it from me.
   Ariel.   Presently ?
   Pros. Ay, with a twink.
   Ariel. Before you can say " come " and " go,"
And breathe twice and cry " so, so,"
Each one, tripping on his toe,
Will be here with mop and mow.
               [*Curling his hand into* PROSPERO'S.
Do you love me, master ? no ?
   Pros. [*caressing him*]. Dearly, my delicate Ariel.
        [ARIEL *seems to flit away, swiftly and lightly.*
   Pros. [*to* FERDINAND *and* MIRANDA]. No tongue !
all eyes ! be silent !
               [*Soft music, and* IRIS *glides in.*
   Iris. Ceres, most bounteous lady, thy rich leas
Of wheat, rye, barley, vetches, oats, and pease ;
Thy turfy mountains, where live nibbling sheep,

---

38. *Mop and mow*, Grimaces. He thinks of the feigned expressions
   and gestures of actors.
45. *Iris.* The messenger of Juno. The rainbow was the bridge on
   which she crossed from heaven to earth.

And flat meads thatch'd with stover, them to keep ;
50 Thy banks with pioned and twilled brims,
Which spongy April at thy hest betrims,
To make cold nymphs chaste crowns ; and thy broom-
    groves,
Whose shadow the dismissed bachelor loves,
Being lass-lorn ; thy pole-clipt vineyard ;
And thy sea-marge, sterile and rocky-hard,
Where thou thyself dost air ;—the queen o' the sky,
Whose watery arch and messenger am I,
Bids thee leave these, and with her sovereign grace,
60 Here on this grass-plot, in this very place,
To come and sport : her peacocks fly amain :
Approach, rich Ceres, her to entertain.

[Enter Ceres.*]*

Ceres. Hail, many-colour'd messenger, that ne'er
Dost disobey the wife of Jupiter ;
Who with thy saffron wings upon my flowers
Diffusest honey-drops, refreshing showers,
And with each end of thy blue bow dost crown
My bosky acres and my unshrubb'd down,
70 Rich scarf to my proud earth ; why hath thy queen
Summon'd me hither, to this short-grass'd green ?

Iris. A contract of true love to celebrate ;
And some donation freely to estate
On the blest lovers.   High'st queen of state,
Ceres.
Great Juno, comes ; I know her by her gait.

[Enter Juno, *who walks like a goddess and a queen.]*

Juno. How does my bounteous sister ? Go with me
To bless this twain, that they may prosperous be
80 And honour'd in their issue.

---

49. *Stover*, Fodder for cattle in winter.
50. *Pioned*, Perhaps, overgrown with marsh marigolds.
50. *Twilled*, Perhaps, covered with reeds.
62. *Ceres*, Goddess of the harvest.

[They sing.]

Juno. Honour, riches, marriage-blessing,
   Long continuance, and increasing,
   Hourly joys be still upon you !
   Juno sings her blessings on you.

Ceres. Earth's increase, foison plenty,
   Barns and garners never empty,
   Vines with clustering bunches growing,
   Plants with goodly burthen bowing ;

90   Spring come to you at the farthest
   In the very end of harvest !
   Scarcity and want shall shun you ;
   Ceres' blessing so is on you.

   Fer. This is a most majestic vision, and
Harmonious charmingly.   May I be bold
To think these spirits ?
   Pros.   Spirits, which by mine art
I have from their confines call'd to enact
My present fancies.
100   *Fer.*   Let me live here ever ;
So rare a wonder'd father and a wife
Makes this place Paradise.
   [JUNO *and* CERES *whisper, and send* IRIS *on*
      employment.
   Pros. [*to* MIRANDA].   Sweet, now, silence !
Juno and Ceres whisper seriously ;
There's something else to do : hush, and be mute,
Or else our spell is marr'd.
   Iris. You nymphs, called Naiads, of the windring
110   brooks,
With your sedged crowns and ever-harmless looks,
Leave your crisp channels and on this green land

86. *Foison,* Abundance.   112. *Crisp,* Curled.

Answer your summons ; Juno does command :
Come, temperate nymphs, and help to celebrate
A contract of true love ; be not too late.

[*Enter certain* Nymphs.]

You sunburnt sicklemen, of August weary,
Come hither from the furrow and be merry :
Make holiday ; your rye-straw hats put on
120 And these fresh nymphs encounter every one
In country footing.

[*Enter certain* Reapers, *properly habited : they join
    with the* Nymphs *in a graceful dance ; towards the
    end whereof* PROSPERO *starts suddenly, and speaks,
    after which, to a strange, hollow, and confused noise,
    they heavily vanish.*]

   Pros. [*to* FERDINAND]. You do look, my son, in a
        moved sort,
As if you were dismay'd : be cheerful, sir.
130 Our revels now are ended.   These our actors,
As I foretold you, were all spirits, and
Are melted into air, into thin air :
And, like the baseless fabric of this vision,
The cloud-capp'd towers, the gorgeous palaces,
The solemn temples, the great globe itself,
Yea, all which it inherit, shall dissolve
And, like this insubstantial pageant faded,
Leave not a rack behind.   We are such stuff
As dreams are made on, and our little life
140 Is rounded with a sleep.   Sir, I am vex'd ;
Bear with my weakness ; my old brain is troubled :
Be not disturb'd with my infirmity :
If you be pleased, retire into my cell

126. *Heavily*, Sadly.   128. *Sort*, Way.
136. *Inherit*, Possess   138. *Rack*, Cloud.

And there repose : a turn or two I'll walk,
To still my beating mind.

Mir.   We wish you peace.

    They go out together.   ARIEL *darts in and clings*
      to PROSPERO.

CURTAIN

THE GUEST AT THE BANQUET

(From *Macbeth*)

PERSONS OF THE PLAY

MACBETH, *King of Scotland, who has murdered the former king.*

LADY MACBETH.

BANQUO, *of whom it has been prophesied that his children shall be kings.*

FLEANCE, *his son.*

ROSS, LENNOX, *and other* Scottish lords.

Two Murderers.

Attendants.

Situation.—Macbeth, urged by the prophecy of three witches and the ambition of his wife, has foully murdered the King of Scotland, and obtained the throne. He greatly fears Banquo, whose children, it was said, should be kings, and resolves to take his life.

Time of the events of the play : eleventh century.
Time occupied in acting the play : half an hour.

NOTE ON COSTUME, ETC.

The dress of the men consists of a tunic of some woven material, either plain or pleated below the waist (forming the early equivalent to the Highland kilt), a broad leather belt adorned with studs of metal or a Celtic pattern of interlacing lines, and hose bound with thongs

of leather passed below the foot and brought criss-cross
to the thigh. Macbeth is crowned with a narrow golden
crown. Lady Macbeth wears a long robe, girdled round
the waist, and fastened in front with a great Celtic
brooch. Sargent's portrait of Ellen Terry as Lady Macbeth, wearing the dress which enchanted Burne-Jones,
should be studied by a stage dressmaker who wants a
good model to work on. Both sexes wear jewelled ornaments—rings, armlets, and brooches of bronze and gold.
The Murderers should be dishevelled and uncouth in
appearance.

The representation of the ghost depends very much on
the distance of the stage from the audience, and the
lighting the manager has at his disposal. No one sees
the apparition but Macbeth, and, in the modern theatre,
it is sometimes deemed more effective to make no attempt
to show it to the audience. But it certainly appeared in
Shakespeare's theatre. It is not, of course, a shrouded
figure, but Banquo in the dress in which he lies dead on
the road at the time of the banquet to which he has come
according to promise, his face ghastly pale, and streaked
with blood from his wounds.

SCENE I

A room in MACBETH'S *castle at Forres. The furniture is of the simplest kind : a chest, a state seat, a
bench, shaped from unpolished wood. Across the seat
lies the pelt of some wild animal. On the bench sits*
BANQUO, *as if deep in thought.*

Ban. Thou hast it now : king, Cawdor, Glamis,
    all,
As the weird women promised, and, I fear,
10 Thou play'dst most foully for it : yet it was said
It should not stand in thy posterity,
But that myself should be the root and father
Of many kings. If there come truth from them—
As upon thee, Macbeth, their speeches shine—
May they not be my oracles as well,

And set me up in hope ?   But hush ! no more
[*He rises and stands at the sound of a sennet.*

[*Enter* MACBETH, *as king*, LADY MACBETH, *as
queen*, LENNOX, ROSS, *and* Attendants.]

20   *Macb.* [*greeting* BANQUO]. Here's our chief guest.
    Lady M.   If he had been forgotten,
It had been as a gap in our great feast,
And all-thing unbecoming.
    Macb. To-night we hold a solemn supper, sir.
And I'll request your presence.
    Ban.   Let your highness
Command upon me ; to the which my duties
Are ever knit.
    Macb. Ride you this afternoon ?
30   *Ban.* Ay, my good lord.
    Macb. We should have else desired your good
        advice,
Which still hath been most grave and prosperous,
In this day's council ; but we'll take to-morrow.
[*Casually*] Is't far you ride ?
    Ban. As far, my lord, as will fill up the time
'Twixt this and supper : go not my horse the better,
I must become a borrower of the night
For a dark hour or twain.
40   *Macb.*   Fail not our feast.
    Ban. My lord, I will not.
    Macb.   Hie you to horse : adieu,
Till you return at night.   Goes Fleance with you ?
    Ban. Ay, my good lord : our time does call upon's.
    Macb. I wish your horses swift and sure of foot ;
And so I do command you to their backs.
Farewell !   [BANQUO *bows and goes out.*
Let every man be master of his time
Till seven at night : to make society

23. *All-thing*, Together.   24. *Solemn*, Ceremonial.
33. *Still*, Always.

50 The sweeter welcome, we will keep ourself
 Till supper-time alone : while then, God be with you !
   [*Exeunt all but* MACBETH *and one* Attendant.
 Sirrah, a word with you : attend those men
 Our pleasure ?
  Atten. They are, my lord, without the palace gate.
  Macb. Bring them before us.   [*Exit* Attendant.
         To be thus is nothing.
 But to be safely thus.—Our fears in Banquo
 Stick deep ; and in his royalty of nature
60 Reigns that which would be fear'd : 'tis much he
   dares ;
 And, to that dauntless temper of his mind,
 He hath a wisdom that doth guide his valour
 To act in safety. There is none but he
 Whose being I do fear : and, under him,
 My Genius is rebuked ; as, it is said,
 Mark Antony's was by Cæsar. He chid the sisters
 When first they put the name of king upon me,
 And bade them speak to him : then prophet-like
70 They hail'd him father to a line of kings :
 Upon my head they placed a fruitless crown,
 And put a barren sceptre in my gripe,
 Thence to be wrench'd with an unlineal hand,
 No son of mine succeeding. If't be so,
 For Banquo's issue have I filed my mind ;
 For them the gracious Duncan have I murder'd ;
 Put rancours in the vessel of my peace
 Only for them ; and mine eternal jewel
 Given to the common enemy of man,
80 To make them kings, the seed of Banquo kings !
 Rather than so, come fate into the list,

---

66. *Genius.* According to the old Roman belief, the guardian spirit
 of man, coming into existence with him at birth, and ac-
 companying him throughout his life. A soothsayer warns
 Antony against the power of the genius of Octavius Cæsar
 to daunt his, in *Antony and Cleopatra*, II. iii.
75. *Filed*, Defiled.

And champion me to the utterance !   [*Starting*] Who's
    there ?

[*Enter the* Attendant, *and the two* Murderers.]

Now go to the door, and stay there till we call.
                               [*Exit* Attendant.
Was it not yesterday we spoke together ?
    First Mur. It was, so please your highness.
    Macb. [*eying them narrowly*]. Well then, now
90 Have you consider'd of my speeches ?   Know
That it was *he* in the times past which held you
So under fortune, which you thought had been
Our innocent self ?
    First Mur.   You made it known to us.
    Macb. I did so, and went further, which is now
Our point of second meeting.   Do you find
Your patience so predominant in your nature
That you can let this go ?   Are you so gospell'd
To pray for this good man and for his issue,
100 Whose heavy hand hath bow'd you to the grave
And beggar'd yours for ever ?
    Sec. Mur.   I am one, my liege,
Whom the vile blows and buffets of the world
Have so incensed that I am reckless what
I do to spite the world.
    First Mur.   And I another
So weary with disasters, tugg'd with fortune,
That I would set my life on any chance,
To mend it, or be rid on't.
110   *Macb.*   Both of you
Know Banquo was your enemy.   So is he mine
And every minute of his being thrusts
Against my near'st of life ; and thence it is
That I to your assistance do make love,

---

        82. *Champion me*, Fight against me in single combat.
        82. *To the utterance*, To the very end, to death.
        102. *My liege*, My lord.

Masking the business from the common eye
For sundry weighty reasons.

Sec. Mur.   We shall, my lord,
Perform what you command us.

First Mur.   Though our lives—

120 *Macb.* Your spirits shine through you. Within
        this hour at most
I will advise you—for't must be done to-night,
And something from the palace—and with him
Fleance his son, that keeps him company,
Whose absence is no less material to me
Than is his father's, must embrace the fate
Of that dark hour.   Resolve yourselves apart .
I'll come to you anon.

First Mur.   We are resolv'd, my lord.

130 *Macb.* I'll call upon you straight : abide within.

                        [*Exeunt* Murderers.
It is concluded.   Banquo, thy soul's flight,
If it find heaven, must find it out to-night.

CURTAIN

SCENE II

*Near the Castle of Forres. If possible, play the
scene in semi-darkness, as it should represent a stormy
twilight.   There are streaks of red in the west, but the
sky is rainy and wild.*

[*Enter the* Murderers.]

First Mur. The west yet glimmers with some
        streaks of day :
Now spurs the lated traveller apace
10 To gain the timely inn ; and near approaches
The subject of our watch.

Sec. Mur.   Hark ! I hear horses.

[*They crouch at one side of the stage, as if listening
        and waiting. The sound of horses' hoofs is
        heard without.*

Banquo's voice. Give us a light there, ho !

Sec. Mur.   Then 'tis he : the rest
That are within the note of expectation
Already are i' the court.

20   *First Mur.* [*listening*]. His horses go about.

Sec. Mur. Almost a mile : but he does usually,
So all men do, from hence to the palace gate
Make it their walk.

First Mur.   A light, a light !

[*They shrink farther into hiding, as* BANQUO *and*
        FLEANCE *come in,* FLEANCE *carrying a torch.*

Sec. Mur.   'Tis he.

First Mur. Stand to't.

Ban. It will be rain to-night.

30   *First Mur.*   Let it come down.

[*Springs out of hiding and attacks* BANQUO, *forcing
        him to the ground.*

Ban. [*in the voice of a man who can only just speak*].
            O treachery ! Fly, good Fleance, fly, fly, fly !
Thou mayst revenge.   [*Groaning*] O slave !   [*Dies.*

Sec. Mur. Who did strike out the light ?

First Mur.   Was't not the way ?

Sec. Mur. There's but one down ; the son is fled.

First Mur.   We have lost
40 Best half of our affair.

Sec. Mur. Well, let's away, and say how much is
done.   [*They go out, leaving* BANQUO *lying dead.*

---

12. *Horses.* The sound of their hoofs is imitated with half coco-
    nut shells on a flat stone.

SCENE III

*A room in the castle. On a trestle table a feast is set
out. The bowls, candelabra, drinking cups, platters,
etc., should be as far as possible of the Celtic pattern.
Benches are set at the table for the guests. It should
stand at the back of the stage, leaving room in front for the
" aside" scenes between* MACBETH *and the* Murderer,
and MACBETH *and* LADY MACBETH. *Right is a state
seat, or throne, occupied by* LADY MACBETH *at the be-*
10 *ginning of the scene.* MACBETH *goes forward to welcome
the guests,* ROSS, LENNOX, *etc. Attendants stand ready
to serve the banquet. Music plays as the curtain goes up.*

Macb. You know your own degrees; sit down: at first
And last the hearty welcome.
    Lords.   Thanks to your majesty.
    Macb. Ourself will mingle with society,
And play the humble host.
Our hostess keeps her state, but in best time
We will require her welcome.
20   *Lady M.* Pronounce it for me, sir, to all our friends;
For my heart speaks they are welcome.
        [*She descends from the state seat, or throne, and goes
          to the table.*

    [*Enter* Murderer, *and stands in the shadow of the
             throne.*]

    Macb. See, they encounter thee with their hearts'
           thanks
Both sides are even: here I'll sit i' the midst:
Be large in mirth; anon we'll drink a measure

      18. *State,* A state seat with a canopy.

30 The table round. [*Going to the* Murderer, *and speak-
    ing to him in what appears to be a low tone, in
    which horror and warning are mingled*] There's
    blood upon thy face.

Mur. [*imperturbably*]. 'Tis Banquo's then.

Macb. 'Tis better thee without than he within.
Is he dispatch'd ?

Mur. My lord, his throat is cut ; that I did for him.

Macb. Thou art the best o' the cut-throats : yet
    he's good
40 That did the like for Fleance : if thou didst it,
Thou art the nonpareil.

Mur.   Most royal sir,
Fleance is 'scaped.

Macb. [*pressing his hands to his head*]. Then comes
    my fit again : I had else been perfect,
Whole as the marble, founded as the rock,
As broad and general as the casing air :
But now I am cabin'd, cribb'd, confin'd, bound in
To saucy doubts and fears.   But Banquo's safe ?
50 *Mur.* Ay, my good lord : safe in a ditch he bides,
With twenty trenchèd gashes on his head ;
The least a death to nature.

Macb.   Thanks for that :
There the grown serpent lies ; the worm that's fled
Hath nature that in time will venom breed,
No teeth for the present.   Get thee gone : to-morrow
We'll hear, ourselves, again.   [*Exit* Murderer.

    [LADY MACBETH *leaves the table and crosses to her
        husband, who stands in a reverie of anguish.*
60 *Lady M.*   My royal lord,
You do not give the cheer : the feast is sold
That is not often vouch'd, while 'tis a-making ;
From home the sauce to meat is ceremony ;
Meeting were bare without it.

---

41. *Nonpareil*, One without equal.   54. *Worm*, Serpent.
62. *Vouch'd*, Guaranteed (good). She is thinking of hospitable
    exhortations to eat and drink.

Macb.   Sweet remembrancer !
    [*Goes to the table and speaks to his guests.*
Now, good digestion wait on appetite,
And health on both !

Len.   May't please your highness sit.

70 [*Enter the* Ghost *of* BANQUO, *and sits in* MACBETH'S
       place.]

Macb. Here had we now our country's honour
   roof'd,
Were the graced person of our Banquo present ;
Who may I rather challenge for unkindness
Than pity for mischance !

Ross.   His absence, sir,
Lays blame upon his promise. Please't your highness
To grace us with your royal company.

80 *Macb.* The table's full.

Len.   Here is a place reserved, sir.

Macb. Where ?

Len. Here, my good lord. [MACBETH *starts back in
   horror, clutching his breast*] What is't that moves
   your highness ?

Macb. [*in a tremulous, gasping voice*]. Which of you
   have done this ?

Lords.   What, my good lord ?

Macb. [*crying out to the* Ghost]. Thou canst not say
90   I did it : never shake
Thy gory locks at me.
   [*Flinging out his arm to shut the vision from his
    eyes, he staggers from the table.*

Ross. Gentlemen, rise ; his highness is not well.

Lady M. [*calming the guests*]. Sit, worthy friends :
   my lord is often thus,
And hath been from his youth : pray you, keep seat ;
He will again be well : if much you note him,
You shall offend him and extend his passion :
100 Feed, and regard him not. [*Approaching* MACBETH]
   Are you a man ?

Macb. Ay, and a bold one, that dare look on that
Which might appal the devil.
     Lady M.   O proper stuff !
This is the very painting of your fear :
This is the air-drawn dagger which, you said,
Led you to Duncan.   O, these flaws and starts,
Impostors to true fear, would well become
A woman's story at a winter's fire,
110 Authorized by her grandam.   Shame itself !
Why do you make such faces ?   When all's done,
You look but on a stool.
     Macb. [*as the* Ghost *rises from his place and passes
          from the table and the room*].   Prithee, see there !
          behold ! look ! lo ! how say you ?
Why, what care I ?   If thou canst nod, speak too.
If charnel-houses and our graves must send
Those that we bury back, our monuments
Shall be the maws of kites.
120   *Lady M.*   What, quite unmann'd in folly ?
     Macb. [*glancing fearfully around*].   If I stand here, I
          saw him.
     Lady M.   Fie, for shame !
     Macb. [*as if in a trance*].   Blood hath been shed ere
          now, i' the olden time,
Ere humane statute purged the gentle weal ;
Ay, and since too, murders have been perform'd
Too terrible for the ear : the time has been,
That, when the brains were out, the man would die,
130 And there an end ; but now they rise again,
With twenty mortal murders on their crowns,
And push us from our stools : this is more strange
Than such a murder is.
     Lady M.   My worthy lord,

104. *Proper*, Fine ; here used contemptuously.
107. *Flaws*, Sudden gusts ; here, of uncontrollable emotion.
117. *Charnel-houses*, Places where the bones of the dead are laid.
126. *Weal*, State.   The expression means " purged it into gentle-
     ness."

Your noble friends do lack you.

> [*Takes his hand to lead him to the table. Suddenly,
> as if reassured by the normality of her tone and
> action, he recovers control of himself, though his
> voice is tired and shaken, like that of a man who
> has endured some terrific strain.*

140

Macb.   I do forget.

[*Goes to the table*] Do not muse at me, my most worthy
     friends ;
I have a strange infirmity, which is nothing
To those that know me. Come, love and health to
     all,
Then I'll sit down. Give me some wine ; fill full.

> [*The* Ghost *stands by the throne, its head bent for-
> ward, one hand clutching its throat.*

150 I drink to the general joy o' the whole table,

> [*Lifts his wine-cup.*

And to our dear friend Banquo, whom we miss ;
Would he were here ! to all, and him, we thirst,
And all to all.

Lords.   Our duties, and the pledge !

> [*They drink.* MACBETH, *suddenly seeing the figure
> by the throne, lets his wine-cup fall, and again
> staggers from his place, one arm lifted as if to
> exorcise the spirit.*

160   *Macb.* Avaunt ! and quit my sight ! let the earth
     hide thee !
Thy bones are marrowless, thy blood is cold ;
Thou hast no speculation in those eyes
Which thou dost glare with !

Lady M.   Think of this, good peers,
But as a thing of custom : 'tis no other ;
Only it spoils the pleasure of the time.

> [*The guests start from the table, regarding* MACBETH
> *in wonder and fear.*

170   *Macb.* What man dare, I dare :

---

160. *Avaunt*, Begone.   163. *Speculation*, Power of seeing.

Approach thou like the rugged Russian bear,
The arm'd rhinoceros, or the Hyrcan tiger ;
Take any shape but that, and my firm nerves
Shall never tremble : or be alive again,
And dare me to the desert with thy sword ;
If trembling I inhabit then, protest me
The baby of a girl.   Hence, horrible shadow !
Unreal mockery, hence !

    [*The* Ghost *passes from the place.*   MACBETH *gives*
180   *a great sobbing sigh, like that with which a man*
        regains consciousness.

                      Why so ; being gone,
I am a man again.   [*Turning blindly towards his guests*]
    Pray you sit still.
    Lady M. [*at his side*].   You have displaced the mirth,
    broke the good meeting,
With most admir'd disorder.
    Macb.   Can such things be,
And overcome us like a summer's cloud,
190 Without our special wonder ?   [*Gazing at her*] You
    make me strange
Even to the disposition that I owe,
When now I think you can behold such sights,
And keep the natural ruby of your cheeks,
When mine is blanch'd with fear.
    Ross.   What sights, my lord ?
    Lady M. [*quickly, returning to the table*].   I pray you,
    speak not ; he grows worse and worse ;
Question enrages him.   At once, good-night :
200 Stand not upon the order of your going,
But go at once.
    Len.   Good-night : and better health
Attend his majesty !

172. *Hyrcan.*   Hyrcania, south of the Caspian, famed for its tigers.
173. *Nerves,* Sinews.
176. *Inhabit,* Dwell, remain.   (Henley compares Milton's use of the
    word—" Meanwhile inhabit lax, ye powers of heaven.")
187. *Admir'd,* Wondered at.

Lady M. [*as the guests depart*]. A kind good-night to
all !

[*When the last guest has gone she stands as if turned
to stone, staring before her, not glancing at* MAC-
BETH, *who has sunk on the steps of the throne.*

210 *Macb.* [*slowly, as if his words were weighted by his
horror*]. It will have blood ; they say, blood will
have blood :

Stones have been known to move and trees to speak ;
Augurs and understood relations have
By magot-pies and choughs and rooks brought forth
The secret'st man of blood.   What is the night ?

Lady M. [*in a dull, expressionless voice*]. Almost at
odds with morning, which is which.

Macb. [*clutching at the foot of the throne*]. For mine
own good,

220 All causes shall give way ; I am in blood
Stepp'd in so far that, should I wade no more,
Returning were as tedious as go o'er.

Lady M. [*in the same toneless voice*]. You lack the
season of all natures, sleep.

Macb. [*rising*]. Come, we'll to sleep . . . [*goes slowly
towards her, groping for her hand*] . . . we'll to
sleep.

CURTAIN

213. *Augurs*, Soothsayers.
213. *Understood relations*, The mystical bearing of certain things
     upon one another, understood by the soothsayer—who knows
     the meaning of the flight of birds, the way in which the stars
     influence the fate of man, and so on.
214. *Magot-pies*, Magpies.
214. *Choughs*, Jackdaws.

LITTLE PLAYS FROM SHAKESPEARE

Selected and Arranged by EVELYN SMITH, B.A.

<u>T.E.S. 104</u>

FIRST SERIES

The Tricking of Malvolio (from *Twelfth Night*)—The Shrew Tamed (from *The Taming of the Shrew*)—The Adventure on Gadshill (from *Henry IV.*, Part I.)—The English Traitors (from *Henry V.*)—The Soldier and the King (from *Henry V.*)—The Pound of Flesh (from *The Merchant of Venice*)—A Lamentable Comedy (from *A Midsummer Night's Dream*)—The Masque for Miranda (from *The Tempest*)—The Guest at the Banquet (from *Macbeth*).

<u>T.E.S. 106</u>

SECOND SERIES

The Students of Navarre (from *Love's Labour's Lost*) —The Shepherds' Festival (from *The Winter's Tale*)— Dear Lady Disdain (from *Much Ado About Nothing*)— The Feast of Capulet (from *Romeo and Juliet*)—A Day at Ephesus (from *The Comedy of Errors*)—Great Cæsar's Death (from *Julius Cæsar*)—The Queen and the Cardinal (from *Henry VIII.*).

Full Acting Notes and advice on
Costume and Presentation.

THOMAS NELSON AND SONS, LTD.

THE APPROACH TO SHAKESPEARE

A Pleasant Introduction to the Greater Plays with a Short Life of the Poet

By Mrs. ANDREW LANG

With Frontispiece Portrait from the Droeshout Engraving

¶ The Contents of this Volume comprise :—

i. A charming Biography of Shakespeare, followed by a Biographical Sketch of Charles and Mary Lamb, specially written for children by Mrs. Andrew Lang.

ii. Select Stories from Lamb's *Tales from Shakespeare*, Holinshed's *Chronicle*, Plutarch's *Lives*, and Scott's *Tales of a Grandfather*.

iii. Poetical Extracts from the Plays, following the various stories.

¶ The Plays included are : *A Midsummer Night's Dream ; King John ; The Merchant of Venice ; Richard II.; As You Like It ; Julius Cæsar ; Twelfth Night ; Richard III.; The Tempest ;* and *Macbeth.*

¶ The Book is, therefore, not merely Shakespeare and Lamb coupled together, but a carefully planned introduction to the chief plays read in schools, histories as well as comedies. The story of Macbeth is given by Lamb and Scott respectively, for comparative purposes.

¶ The numerous Illustrations are particularly interesting and helpful, and include pen-pictures of Shakespeare's haunts, portraits of Charles and Mary Lamb, etc.

THOMAS NELSON AND SONS, Ltd.

NELSON'S
SCHOOL SHAKESPEARE

Edited by Sir HENRY NEWBOLT,
EVELYN SMITH, and JOHN HAMPDEN

Equally suitable for Examinations and
Literary Study

This edition is intended for those teachers who consider that the dramatic side of the poet's genius has recently been over-emphasized, and who remember that Shakespeare was a poet as well as a dramatist.

The Glossary takes the form of footnotes ; the Illustrated Introduction gives enough information to help the reader to visualize the period ; the Text is followed by a Commentary dealing with all the questions raised by the play.

THOMAS NELSON AND SONS, Ltd.

T.E.S. 55

EARLIER ENGLISH DRAMA

Edited by F. J. TICKNER, B.A.

Enlarged Edition

This volume gives examples of English Drama from the Mummers to *Everyman*, tracing its development through the Miracle and Mystery Plays, and Interludes to the later Moralities; every part of the country being represented, and local differences emphasized. Illustrated.

T.E.S. 156

SHAKESPEARE'S PREDECESSORS

Long Extracts from Elizabethan Playwrights

Edited by F. J. TICKNER, B.A.

The selected scenes are from plays by John Heywood, Nicholas Udall, Thomas Sackville, John Lyly, Thomas Kyd, Robert Greene, and Christopher Marlowe. With suggestions for Staging.

THOMAS NELSON AND SONS, LTD.